LISTEN, GENTILE !

LISTEN, GENTILE!

The Story of a Life

by

Y. BEN AHARON

NEW YORK   TORONTO

STAPLES PRESS LIMITED

CAVENDISH PLACE · LONDON · W1

FIRST PUBLISHED 1947

BOOK
PRODUCTION
WAR ECONOMY
STANDARD

*This book is produced in complete
conformity with the authorised
economy standards*

SET IN 12 LINOTYPE GRANJON

Made and printed in England by
STAPLES PRESS LIMITED
at their Bayswater, London, establishment

PREFATORY NOTE

*This story was written in the year
nineteen hundred and forty-four
while the author was a Prisoner
of War at Oflag 79 (Brunswick)
Germany.*

*Of the many friends – including
the publishers – who have helped
him in this work, the author
wishes to name in particular the
late Captain H. A. Buck, M.C.,
whose recent death in an air accident has cut short a life of high
purpose and integrity.*

'For Miriam'

CONTENTS

Part One   THE CAPTIVE

Part Two   THE REBEL

Part Three   THE WORKER

PART ONE

THE CAPTIVE

CHAPTER ONE

PRELUDE IN GREECE

I

ON A LATE April night of the year 1941, I found myself with my company acting as military police on the road leading from Thebes to Athens. The Imperial Expeditionary Force was withdrawing from Northern Greece, and the attempt to evacuate the whole force was already under way. Little did I dream that night that I would find myself in the end among those unlucky six or eight thousand troops who, due to mistakes not of their own making, were to be herded into cages and to remain Prisoners of War in German hands for many years to come. On the night in question I had to concentrate on my job: this left me no time to speculate on future developments.

The highway, though metalled, was yet highly inadequate for the needs of that night. Vehicles of all sizes and descriptions, guns, and troops, crowded the road from bank to bank: and in the ditches alongside, the disbanded and disarmed Greek Army of the North struggled dejectedly home. They drove in front of them the herds of cattle which had been collected to feed them; and the skeleton cows and oxen appeared to be urged by an irresistible impulse to mingle with the deadly traffic on the road. Drivers, their nerves on edge, cursed and blasphemed the silly creatures; the stream of rushing vehicles would come to a standstill until we could succeed in unravelling the blockage and give the sign for the resumption of the race for freedom. That, however, was only a part, and a minor one, of our duty. We had been put on the road to look out for German sabotage agents and paratroopers who, according to precedent, might be expected to infiltrate by land or be dropped from above to delay our movements, thus giving the Germans the opportunity of coming down in force and bagging the lot of us before any large-scale evacuations were possible. We kept a sharp look-out, although it was quite hopeless to distinguish friend from foe, even if the latter had ventured to wear the uniform and badges of his own forces. The light, diffused by a starry Greek night, was of little assistance to visibility, for the road wound its serpentine way amidst the bushy slopes of a boulder-strewn countryside. This wrapped itself as deep darkness round the dimly lit vehicles, which screamed under the restraining grip of their brakes on the down-slopes, and ground slowly uphill in a writhing double layer of shadows. To regulate traffic, to give information to officers with regard to the destination of their units, to sort out entanglements, and to check on occasion the identity of the too inquisitive was all very well: but how does one look for potential saboteurs? It's all a farce anyway, I thought, just a matter of luck.

Sergeant Mark, breathing fast, appeared from nowhere to report the arrest of what appeared to be the very thing we were looking for. A truck driving in the wrong direction, that is to the north against the retreating stream, had been stopped by him. On investigation, my sergeant had 'smelt a rat'. Although the driver of the truck appeared to be O.K., the officer in charge was to the sergeant of doubtful nationality. Certainly not English, by the look of it. I did not wait for further details, but followed the sergeant down the incline to where, close by a curve, I saw the shaded headlights of a car. An army vehicle driving against the line of the withdrawal – wasn't that the very thing we had been ordered to watch out for? When I came to the front of the truck, I saw two men in the cone of my flashlight. I had no difficulty in making out the driver. He was grimy and dishevelled, with a lock of blond hair hanging over his forehead. The first word I heard him utter – wisely to nobody in particular – left no doubt that his home was within easy reach of Bow Bells. Next to him stood an officer – a second lieutenant, as I made sure – of a dark complexion, neatly dressed, and obviously uncomfortable.

'Where are you going to?' I asked.

'I have orders to proceed to Corinth', replied a rasping voice in a strong foreign accent.

'Corinth? If I know anything of the geography of Greece, you are moving away from it . . . and if you keep on the way you are going, you'll get to Berlin!'

'I thought we were moving in the wrong direction,' a now agitated and stuttering voice admitted, 'but my driver assured me we were on the right track, since he had made the same trip only a fortnight ago.'

'Excuse me, Sir,' the driver butted in, 'I must 'ave missed the turn to the left. It is 'ard to find yer way on a night like this, with all the civvies giving you different advice like.'

'What's in the truck?'

'Fifteen O.R's of a Palestine Pioneer unit,' the officer replied. 'We were instructed to establish supply dumps somewhere near Corinth. The remainder of our convoy must have gone on in the right direction when a passing convoy separated us.'

'May I see your identity card?'

He fumbled with his wallet – well stocked, as I made out when he held it close to the car's lights – and handed it to me. 'British Forces, Middle East; Name: Reuben Bar Shalom. Rank: 2/Lt., Auxiliary Military Pioneer Corps', etc., etc.

I thanked him, and returned the card: and having examined the truck with the men – slightly alarmed, I thought – huddled inside, I advised him strongly not to lose his way again, and admonished the driver for not paying more attention to the directions given him by the officer in charge. Then I gave them a gruff 'goodnight', and left it to my sergeant to manœuvre them on to the buzzing road as best he could. 'Poor beggar,' I thought, 'must have had a hard time trying to impose himself on the driver, who presumably felt himself superior to any bloody foreigner, pip or no pip.'

Dawn came at last, suddenly and unheralded: for we had no view to the east. The stream of traffic had steadily dwindled to a trickle. Our work was over, and it suddenly occurred to me for the first time that I knew nothing about my own destination. Between us and the Germans, as I had gathered from a voice which came to me in a drawling sleepy tone out of a passing staff car, there was only the rearguard: and I had to make up my mind whither to direct my company. There could be no question about an embarkation at the Piræus. The port had been severely hit – and I knew something about the priority list for the few boats that would clear that harbour. Hadn't I heard something of a supply dump at Corinth? Of course – the encounter with the suspect truck and its officer came back to me. Now for the Peloponnese, across the bridge of the Gulf – let's hope it would still be intact – and then for a harbour at the Southern tip of Greece.

We boarded our vehicles, which we had kept well hidden and fully stocked, out of sight and touch, and moved off at top speed. The buzzing of Stukas and Messerschmidts could already be heard; and it was imperative to reach shelter on the other side of the Straits of Corinth before the morning mist lifted and revealed

our whereabouts to the preying vultures above. At the several
turning points I came to realise how easy it was to lose one's direction: but we found the bridge without mishap, and on the advice
of an M.P. we crawled into a gorge just outside the town, because,
as he said, a Luftwaffe formation had been seen flying in a
southerly direction, and might catch us on their way back. The
narrow-gauge railway was still in operation, although several
trains had been machine-gunned going south, while ack-ack batteries barked to heaven at random intervals. If trains kept on
moving, why not we? So with a good breakfast inside us we set
off again on the highway, which appeared to be strangely deserted.

A few Messerschmidts soon provided the answer to the puzzle:
and having escaped serious damage, we lay up again till dusk.
Then the road came to life. Hundreds of vehicles crawled on to
the highway from their hiding places, and, squeezing my own
convoy in between, we were off on the race to the port. After some
hard driving we reached Argos on the S.E. tip of the Peloponnese
at dawn. The place and its surroundings were suggestive of
Hellas' past, and the day we spent on the hills to evade German
air observation, revealed to us the peculiar topography which contributed to the strength and failings of the Spartan character. A
pre-arranged signal, calling all unit commanders to a conference,
reminded me that my present sojourn on Sparta's soil was not for
scholarly purposes. Our urgent need was not to stay and muse
upon ancient shrines, but to put as much mileage as possible
between ourselves and them, and escape the talons of the enemy.

The conference called by the brigadier in charge of evacuation
was held in a foul-reeking stable. The brigadier and his staff were
anxious to get the fleeing mass under control, and to fix a list of
priorities for the boats which were expected to anchor at Naphleon
– the port of Argos – that very night. Waiting for embarkation,
we heard, were about 15,000 British and Allied troops, including
about 2,000 Yugoslav officers who had marched on foot the whole
way down from Macedonia to the tip of the Peloponnese. All
things being equal, the bulk of them might expect to embark that
night, and as for the remainder, there was still hope that they
would get away the following night, provided the Germans still
did not molest us. We were urgently reminded to remain in
hiding till dusk, because German aircraft were busily engaged in
tracking down our embarkation points.

I was grateful for a rest, and tramped back to a place which I had the foresight to camouflage. I lay down on my pack and great-coat, and tried to sleep: but in spite of my fatigued limbs and mind (for I had had no sleep for several nights in succession) oblivion did not come to me. I dozed off for a while, but my mind was invaded by beings and events which the very earth I was resting on appeared to conjure up for my benefit. Hot mêlées between Spartans and Athenians, Homeric expostulations, the smoke and cries rising from burning ships faded to a sudden calm from which a shapely and provoking goddess emerged, chased by a misshapen and squat philosopher, to complete my bewilder-ment. In the back of my mind I felt a wish that I had paid less attention to my tutor – an enthusiast for everything Hellenic – and had followed instead the lead of my professor, who had tried hard to win us over to Rome and her genius for constructive and practical thought. Had I followed his lead, I should I felt, have been immune from hedonistic daydreams . . .

I woke with a start to realise that the knockings I had thought to come from inside me were rather of a very material nature. Stones and dust were rolling down, on and over me, stirred up, as I soon found out to my dismay, by a couple of officers sliding down the slope making a bee-line for my little shelter.

'Hi! You up there! Look out!' I shouted, just in time to avert a collision.

They apologised handsomely: then one of them – vaguely familiar to me – checked himself, sized me up, and said:

'Excuse me, Captain – I believe we have met before; the last time not so long ago!'

The voice and foreign intonation sounded even more familiar, but I still failed to place the association. He tried to help me.

'You do not seem to recollect? May I remind you that I had my identity checked by you not far from Thebes; and I am much obliged for the advice you gave me and my obstinate driver.'

The incident came back to me.

'It's quite all right. War, you know . . .' With that I thought to have dismissed the affair, and turned to clean up the mess of stones and dirt which had fallen on my lair. Having satisfied myself that all was in order, I put my head on my pack; but to my surprise I saw the two of them still lingering, whispering ex-citedly. Presently the Man of Thebes came back and said:

'Excuse me, would you be so kind as to lend me your ear for a few minutes?'

'Yes, of course . . .' What the hell was the trouble now I wondered. I invited them to sit down, and the officer who did all the talking introduced himself as Reuben Bar Shalom, and then introduced his pal, whose name I never remembered.

'Captain . . . I am afraid I had not the honour of . . .'

'Sorry, Ranken's my name.' I began to feel a slight irritation rising in my gorge.

'Well, Captain Ranken,' Reuben opened, seating himself and moving a stone to support his elbow, 'I wonder whether you will be willing to tender us advice, and if possible to help us extricate ourselves from an awkward position. We have here with us possibly over a thousand Palestinian troops, whose chances of being evacuated seem to me very slender indeed.'

'I'm sorry to hear that, and I'll be only too pleased to do what I can – although I myself am stranded here, and have no intimate knowledge of the people in charge.'

'By the way, have you ever been to Palestine? I mean recently, and in uniform?'

'Indeed I have, and my recollections of the country are still fresh with me.'

'I thought as much, although I cannot remember definitely if I came across you. Physical associations are often deceptive, particularly in the case of uniformed Englishmen – they look so much alike to the uninitiated. However, I must come to the point.'

While Reuben – for from that day onwards that is how I addressed him – struggled on with his bookish English, interlarded with funny mispronunciations, I had the leisure to take my first thorough look at him.

It was not easy to make him out from his features. A certain buoyancy and alertness made him appear younger than his years; for on closer inspection one became aware of deep lines and wrinkles on the bold forehead and round the brown-green eyes. These looked deeper than a mere thirty-odd years would warrant. Dark, thin, dull hair with just a streak of grey, brushed back in a haphazard way, crowned a fanatical face. But there was in his hair, and particularly in his untrimmed moustache, a strong tinge of dark ginger which went well with his somewhat rubicund face. A longish, narrow head, well formed, ran into pointed lower face features somewhat weakened by a budding double chin. Nose, ears, and teeth were well formed, but strikingly small in size. He was slender in body, yet his gait was robust and very confident. His hands, which one could not fail to notice even when he was not talking, were the most peculiar I had ever seen. They looked like stumps, short fingered and knotty around the knuckles; they were broad and muscular like those of a farm-hand. When he took his leave an hour or so later, I was impressed by the dry hearty grip of those hands. All told, my first survey of his features proved to be unsatisfactory: and this was probably to blame for the time it took me to realise that this was the start of a long and warm friendship.

While my eyes were busy summing up my acquaintance, my ears listened to his case. I noticed that, despite his formal and stiff style, he managed to make his points clear and precise. He spoke on a topic of whose actuality nobody was better aware than myself. My own position was not very different from his: and yet I had to admit to myself that his case, and that of his compatriots, had its peculiarities. He was, I learnt, sceptical about the chances of having his men evacuated. A colonel whom he had interviewed was not helpful, and moreover told Reuben right out that fighting troops must come first. Only after the last man of the fighting units – be they British or otherwise – was safe on board ship, would the turn come for the auxiliary military services, to which all of Reuben's men belonged.

'I have no experience of the traditions of the British Army', he said, 'and do not know on what grounds one service is classified as "fighting" and another as not. My unit, for instance – classed as non-fighting by the colonel – has been employed on several fighting tasks, as our casualty list would prove. At any rate, when your government left us no alternative other than the auxiliary forces, we were given to understand that no discrimination would be made under any circumstances. I grant you that anybody who trusts in a pledge by any government in the world has only himself to blame! I may just as well admit it to you: no matter what the pledge, we would have enlisted – you know we have some scores to settle with Germany, which are of a different character from your own. Well, to cut a long story short, we are saddled now with a few hundred lads who left Germany not so long ago, and whose relatives are still in bondage there, something must be done to have them at least on the priority list for evacuation. The colonel I interviewed had no time for my puerile English – not that I blame him – and I am approaching you with the request to put to him their particular case.'

He won my sympathy at once, but what could I do? I hated to disappoint him, and promised to be on the alert should any opening for intervention offer itself.

Reuben thanked me profusely, and expressed his hope that, should I come to Palestine, I might deliver to his friends the old warrior greeting of the legions to Cæsar. With that, Reuben and his friend – a blond taciturn chap – took their leave to pay a call on their troops somewhere around the mountain side.

II

Just before dusk, I sneaked down through groves and copses to the harbour. People were on the move to their rendezvous. In a short space of time I had my unit together, and on a bugle signal we marched off to take our place in the queue for embarkation. A major on the staff went round the units, and delivered to the unit commanders their embarkation tickets. He appeared to be optimistic, as the arrival of a big convoy of ships and naval craft was expected. The boat assigned to my unit was a big liner of the Empress class. Presently the silhouette of ships approaching the quays and jetty could be made out, and a deep sigh of relief and cheers of admiration for the Navy passed along the ranks.

Then a thudding vibration shook the quay and a babel of voices made us panic for a moment. It was not easy to ascertain what had happened. 'A mine went off somewhere', suggested one, ostensibly in the know: 'Sabotage', opined another: – and so forth. Eventually it was announced that the Empress liner had struck a rock and beached herself. A blunder by the Greek pilot? A deliberate act of sabotage? We shall never know: nor did anyone care about it on that fatal night. It was a major disaster. About three thousand troops – including my own unit – had been destined to be shoved and squeezed into that liner. Now they must remain behind. But that was not all. German aircraft coming over at dawn feasted their eyes on that precious jewel of a ship, which must have told them a comprehensive story. They set the liner on fire, wrecked the quay and railway station, and never lost sight of the place throughout the day. It had to be abandoned and the few thousand troops left behind moved to another port. The Navy had pledged itself to come back for us, cost what it might. No movements of any description could be carried out by day; but nevertheless the amount of work which was done in other ways became apparent when dusk fell again, and we were mercifully hidden from the eyes of our pursuers. In spite of the shortness of my war career, I had been too often the witness and victim of the blunders and inefficiency of my superiors, and was therefore in a position to appreciate merit and vigour of action when I saw it. That was demonstrated to me on the night following the disaster of the Empress liner, when out of nowhere hundreds of vehicles of all types made their appearance. They had been abandoned in ravines, but fortunately not yet destroyed before the embarkation night of Naphleon. What it meant to make those hundreds of vehicles serviceable for a trip at night, along the dreaded Trans-peloponnesian highway and through the Megara pass cannot be over-estimated. Suffice it to say that all troops, to the last man, found their allotted trucks waiting for them. Had that efficient organisation and skill been maintained at the other end, then none of those thousands who represented the last remnant of the I.E.F. in Greece would have fallen into German hands. But this was not to be.

My pen is not able enough to do more than touch upon the experiences of the next forty-eight hours. The memory of the crossing of the Megara pass will remain with me for the rest of my days. That famous highway over the Peloponnesian mountain range became packed with hundreds of vehicles – many indeed without even dim lights – all labouring hard to avoid disaster. The congestion on the narrow dilapidated road was soon to become as much a menace to man and truck as the yawning abysses over which the road hung as if suspended in mid-air. The serpentine windings and sharp turns demanded the highest skill from the drivers of heavy vehicles, even in daylight. At night only good fortune could avoid wholesale disaster. On many occasions I had to light the way for my driver; often my left hand would be holding the torch, while my right hand clutched the door of the truck and my body swung free over the precipice. There, down at the bottom of a three or four hundred foot drop, my eyes beheld the roaring flames devouring a truck that had lost its, at best mira-culous, hold on the road. Injured and panic-stricken men, who had escaped annihilation when their lorries tumbled down the murderous slopes, and had climbed back to the road, made a maddened rush at every passing vehicle with no regard for their own or their drivers' safety. The physical attrition of limbs and nerves, which such a journey entailed, was as nothing compared to the torment of the soul. But the inner experience of that night defies all my attempts at expression. It became part of me, deep and searing, ruthless and cleansing, a tormenting hell and a liberating bliss – a blaze of colours flashing across the past and future patterns of life.

In the morning we made Kalamata, the little town and diminutive jetty on the south western tip. There followed another day of hiding from the Germans and praying for the Navy; our prayer was answered, the Navy turned up against all odds: but an evacuation was not to be. Six thousand officers and men failed to contact the saving arm of the Navy – because they believed and trusted their leaders and superiors. It is not for me to dwell more on the muddle or the crime – call it by whichever name you prefer – which committed six thousand able-bodied and well-armed soldiers of His Majesty's forces to German prison camps. Suffice it to say that two hundred German soldiers managed to occupy the jetty in broad daylight without a shot being fired. Only when darkness fell and the infuriated troops came down from their hiding places, did they hear of the shameful event. Spontaneous action was taken, and the German force was easily overwhelmed. But it was too late. The strong naval force approaching the shore beheld the spectacle of battle, and they paused. Before communications with the Navy were again opened up, the approach of dawn forced the ships to abandon their quest and to look to their own safety. At four-thirty in the morning we were told that a German emissary had asked for and received our surrender. We became prisoners to an enemy who was miles away from us: and three hours were to elapse before the advanced guard came up to deal with us.

While these events followed their course, Reuben did not lose sight of me. He even came to drop the formal 'Captain Ranken' and adopted, tentatively at first, the more intimate 'Jack'. Once left behind at Naphleon, however, nothing more could be done to save his lads from captivity. Their numbers mounted in the end to fourteen hundred; and they marched as a body into bondage for the rest of the war. I lost touch with him, because on the morning of our surrender I made an attempt to escape the impending fate, by marching off with a few pals in an easterly direction. The attempt proved abortive; after having spent four days in the hills overhanging a small fishing port a German patrol caught us, at the moment when we were arguing with the owner of a fishing craft about a yachting trip to Crete, or better still to Egypt.

The Greek army barracks at Corinth had been chosen by our captors to 'house' the prisoners of war – metaphorically speaking, for most of the troops lived for about six weeks in the open. There I was left at last by my German guards – and there it was that my closer contact with Reuben and his crowd began. I was surprised to find Reuben a changed man. He had shed his gloom and ill-foreboding. Once in the clutches of the enemy, he set himself the task of putting heart into his men by donning a mask of seemingly complete unconcern. In close co-operation with a few of his pals, officers of the Palestinian companies, and supported by the most splendid N.C.O. corps I have ever come across, they got themselves organized and showed an undaunted exterior to foe and friend alike: for I regret to say many of the British felt the presence of the Palestinian Jews to be a potential menace to their own fair treatment by the Germans, and let this feeling be apparent. I imagine that, feeling the isolation from without and within, Reuben and his friends were the more grateful for any bit of kindness and consideration shown to them. Although I do not think that I deserved anything of the kind, that feeling must have been at the bottom of the warm welcome Reuben afforded me when I was finally dumped at Corinth.

'Hello, Jack,' he shouted exuberantly, 'I am sorry to see you here! I thought you were floating by now in some dinghy on the open sea. Well, tough luck for you and for all of us! But it's no use crying for lost opportunities. Cheer up, Jack!' He gripped my arm and shouted at me: 'We are all here, and the Nazis are true to form. So far the total is only a matter of seven casualties: one chap was shot for overstepping a trip-wire while trading with Greek vendors, and six other fellows have been shot at and wounded for striking a match at night in that hole which is called "abort" – and I had to carry a load of timber with a mad German clicking his trigger behind my back. Yes, and we had quite a cheerful little interview with a German I.O. No, there is nothing to worry about. The Nazi gentleman assured us that he abhorred Jews' flesh, and that we shouldn't be made into mincemeat for sausages. His taste may change of course, when the Danish pigs have breathed their last. And now let me introduce you to my lads.'

With that he led me off to the dug-outs and trenches which

21

served as camp. On smoky camp fires cooking was in progress. With an imperial wave of his hand Reuben invited me to choose according to taste. Each fire represented a definite and uncompromising cuisine. He mentioned the names of the denominations, such as *à la sauerkraut,* Balkan, French (in honour of the cook – former chef of a Parisian restaurant), *à l'arabe,* and, the most prominent, the *cuisine à la commune,* in honour of their collective settlements in Palestine. As it turned out, all pots contained the same dish of green horse-beans in their jackets.

To this day I don't know how or why I became intrigued with Reuben and his crowd. Although I had spent a few years in Palestine during the riots and after the outbreak of the war, and had seen much of the Zionist settlements, I never took the slightest interest in them. We were far too busy, what with Arab bands and Jewish demonstrations, and I felt resentful about the amount of bother caused by what may have been a noble, but was to me an utterly alien, enterprise. I felt sincere sympathy for the victims of Nazism; but I failed to understand in what way the Jewish work in Palestine would affect the 'Jewish problem', as the Zionists so noisily boasted – yes, boasted to my way of thinking – about its existence.

When I come to think of my frequent conversations with Reuben, stretching over a period of three years as a P.O.W. in Germany – conversations which eventually made me write this book – I realise that my experiences during this war and the shock of captivity must have broken down my inner defences. Mental speculations on political, moral and social problems, which had never troubled me in the past, began slowly to invade my whole being. I have a notion that Reuben was well aware of that process, when, in the course of our conversations, he held up for my benefit the mirror of his generation. We used to meet on our habitual peregrinations round the camp, and air our views on the military situation with its underlying political and social background.

The fact that Reuben appeared to be well-informed and widely read did not surprise me, since I shared with others the general belief in the versatility of the Jewish intellect. But Reuben's views and orations – he had a marked weakness for trailing off into lengthy orations – got hold of me: not so much for the new vistas they opened up, as for the personal note of authority and quick orientation which lent them character and freshness. None of the

familiar political or ethical theories fitted in with his views; and I
think that this fact, more than anything else, broke down my
innate scepticism and sent me off in hot pursuit of his train of
thought. I thought then – and have since confirmed it – that only
hard-won personal experience and a sense of moral values could
have moulded such a profound belief in the destiny of men. Even
on such a matter as the Jewish problem and its international significance – which was the centre of his personal interest – even on
that, he had no time for cant or hackneyed theories. The Jewish
question, and for that matter, any other questions, such as
socialism, and moral codes, were from the start for him matters
of vital importance. 'Thought permeates history but man's actions
make it', was his favourite quotation. True, I often felt irritated,
and thought his attitude part of the Jewish arrogance so generally
believed in, but I was rewarded in the end for my self-control.

III

I remember one conversation in particular which revealed a
fundamental trait in his make-up.

One afternoon Mr. Himmler came to visit our camp. He
appeared to gloat over our miserable surroundings and sounded
one of our friends as to his feelings about Mr. Churchill. He received a fairly spirited reply and withdrew. I made a few remarks
on the Nazi attitude towards the Jews, and maintained that a
good deal of it might be ascribed to their envy of the Jewish intellect. Reuben did not agree with me: he defined Nazi anti-semitism
as cunning propaganda and a method of planting Nazi columns
amongst the Christian and Muslim peoples of the world; an
economic expedient for the distribution of rewards to the hungry
scum amongst Hitler's early followers. But anti-semitism as such
– he emphasised – came into being with the proclamation of the
Decalogue, and particularly with the anti-civilization movement
of the Prophets. As to the intellectual superiority of the Jewish
race – he thought it a myth.

'And a poisonous myth into the bargain. The Jews have no
more brain-power than any other of the civilized races; and
judging by the mess we made of our national and political life,
even the existence of a reasonable average of it might be doubted.
I am not surprised that no Jew has ever repudiated that myth,

which clearly originated among Gentiles; on the contrary, many Jews found in your undeserved compliment – if it was ever meant as such – a welcome compensation for the blatant abnormality of the social and political situation of Jewry. It is remarkable that only nations which have failed in their political or national life fall back on their intellectual superiority. The Germans, for instance, are never more noisy about their *Kultur* than in times of military or political defeat. You British had never any use for such a pretence, because the claim of naval, military or imperial superiority carries more weight than any other boast. To fall back on a claim of intellectual or cultural superiority means to substitute an immeasurable entity for physical superiority. I believe that both biologist and psychologist have neglected to enquire into the all-pervading auto-suggestion of superiority which is practised, in all fields of human activity, by every individual and every human group. I take it as a vital part of our mental make-up, and probably a most essential weapon in the struggle for life and social position. I believe that actual superiority, or if not that, then at least the make-believe of superiority, is indispensable whether for group or individual activities. Look into history, and tell me if you can find any people or class, any god or creed, which has not claimed superiority in morals or in prowess over all others. It did not begin on Mount Sinai, and it will probably not end with the pricking of the bubble of Nazi Aryanism. Between ourselves, don't you and every other Englishman believe in the superiority of your race over all the rest? Is not the popular gibe, that "niggers begin at Calais", a boast of racial superiority? I daresay that until 1918 you had a very legitimate claim for it. But that is beside the point', he hurriedly interjected, when he saw the ominous frown on my face. 'What I am concerned with is to prove to you that the Jews accepted your compliment because there was nothing else left to them to boast of. What other superiority could we claim? State, country, social productivity, military prowess – none of these attributes of a normal people were ours, although we made manifold contributions in every field for others to boast about. We adapted our philosophy to that Gentile misinterpretation, and made of it a glittering flag, but in fact one of no substance."

'But . . .' I tried to put a spoke in his reasoning: 'You can't deny the keen and sharp intellect Jews display, in trade, in the arts, and in many professions?'

'I can and I shall', he retaliated. 'The Jew had to make a living in a permanently hostile world. We won't investigate at present the reason for the manifest hostility of all Gentiles to the Jews. But nobody denies the fact of its existence all through the ages, though in varying degrees of aggressiveness. In order to make a living under such unfavourable conditions, the Jew had to be above the average level of his Gentile rivals in mental acuteness and flexibility. Some of the Jews – I emphasize *some,* because the vast majority of them never reached that level and remained the economic pariahs of Eastern and Western Europe – some of them, I say, climbed up beyond the average level – and at what price? The effort required to reach and to maintain it disfigured their bodies, sapped the joy of life from their wretched existence. The successful became bundles of hypersensitive nerves or calculating machines – and what has that to do with intellectual superiority?'

'But you have still failed to explain to me for instance,' I quickly cut in on him, 'why your grip on political affairs and your quick orientations in the changing kaleidoscope of international conditions are so much more penetrating than mine?'

'Of course I have failed to do it, and I shall never come to it if you keep interrupting me', came his reply, with a mischievous twinkle. 'Now let me explain to you that your belief that my humble versatility in the fleeting affairs of our time is due to some intellectual faculty . . . is a fallacy. I wish it were so, but it isn't. I will try to explain my meaning by analogy. You Britishers, for instance, are amongst the most travelled people in the world: but you travel by plane, and stop at certain places for rest or entertainment, or simply to plant your flag. There are other places at which you never look, because you have found out that there is no profit in it (and I don't mean material profit only). Well, in short, you steer your own course from point to point and skip the remainder. Consequently you know very thoroughly the stations of your flight, and you are consciously – damn it, sometimes proudly – ignorant of the rest. Well, we Jews also travel; but not, as our maligners would have it, of our own volition; only after being kicked out – gently or brutally as the case may be. We have had to go over the globe with a tooth-comb, to enquire like beggars into the lie of the land, reconnoitre, and diffuse the information obtained to warn or to encourage the main army in the rear. I know more about the world, because sections of my people live and have been martyred in every corner of the globe. Look at my boys over there round their camp fires; their brothers and sisters and relatives are spread over fifty countries. In my own settlement there are natives of twenty-four different countries. I must have a fair notion of what it was like in those countries – not to speak of my own wanderings. You learnt geography and history from a book or a pleasure cruise – I got to know ten races before I could read and write properly.

'There is another source of international knowledge with us Jews: you may call it a transcendental one, but I myself call it a biological one. You know how the scars of wounds react to murky weather? They ache, and make you a meteorologist. The scars of my people come from wounds inflicted by a medley of weapons from the Bronze Age onwards (in the age of science we are treated to gas chambers), and they signal to us when the weather gets heavy. And on top of this come the scars from the self-inflicted wounds resulting from fatalism, despair, superstitions, false pretences, and that cursed urge for superiority. They, thank God, were sufficiently raw to sting my own generation, and a generation which preceded mine, into revolt. No, my own generation, or at least a considerable section of it, evaded the trap of intellectual superiority and the empty poisonous myth of being the salt of the earth. My father and I, like those captive friends of mine and their fathers, belong to two different antagonistic camps. I doubt whether you, Jack, would understand. You and your generation can perhaps content yourselves with a new coat of chrome paint on what your fathers were. It is not for me to judge. But we had to rebel, not for the sake of an ideology, but for the sake of our own little selves; and one of the objects of our rebellion was to uproot that myth.'

Reuben broke off, and this time without any interruption from me. Either he was exhausted, or perhaps he realised – what I was already aware of – that the dark mass of humanity on the floor was sound asleep. Mighty snores sawed through his staccato sentences as if to underline their implications.

I was surprised to find Reuben's outpourings of stirring interest. It was not curiosity, I felt, but a spontaneous response to some of his thrusts. Many of us prisoners felt that the Nazi war was a total one in more than a technical administrative sense: we felt we should need new tools to deal with its consequences. The ideals of making money and having a good time, and the 'devil take the hindmost' affectation, were left far behind us. Our minds were keen to come to grips with the malignant cancers of our civilization. Had Reuben's generation any message reaching out beyond its narrow circle? There and then I made up my mind to get his story – if Reuben were willing.

The following morning we got our orders to move. We were glad to get away from vermin and horse-beans, and settle down to our inevitable captive life. As it turned out, Reuben went to a different camp, and it was only after ten months that we met again, in a camp in drab Westphalia.

CHAPTER TWO

APOCALYPTIC PLAYGROUNDS

SETTLED IN A camp in Germany, we had leisure to observe clearly. And circumstances obtruded themselves upon our notice, from which we were forced to draw certain conclusions. As is known, people of my kidney tend to be critical of the written word. The standard of our Press before this war had never been to my taste, since I found little interest in a frantic hunt for sensation, or in the gaudy colouring given to human tragedies and follies. In particular, I and my friends had felt the deepest mistrust at the tales of Nazi horrors. I had been to Germany once or twice for holidays, and the German people impressed me as an honest, hard-working people, though stiff and lacking in humour. I had had no opportunity to see Germany after the Nazis came to power, but it needed more than horror-tales to convince me that such a people would acquiesce in a régime of brutality and savagery, within a few years of Nazi dictatorship. Even now it is difficult for me to understand and comprehend the springs from which their action flows. A German once said to me: 'We are brave soldiers, but cowardly citizens'. That may be part of the explanation. To some extent I had been fortified in my attitude by the official policy of our successive governments, which in pursuing a policy of appeasement and even of active help towards the Nazi government, seemed to imply that the anti-Nazi propaganda had not much to give it foundation. When we declared war on Germany, and the government endorsed the anti-Nazi propaganda, even then it left me cold. I knew that we declared war on Germany in order to break the revived German aggressiveness. I understood something of its consequences, and perceived that it threatened our interests and security – moral as well as physical. But no propaganda could make me hate the Germans. Anyway, to show such a strong emotion was incompatible with my upbringing: I had always been taught to be slightly scornful of emotionalism and hysterics of any kind. If I disliked certain characteristics of foreigners, and tended to keep myself aloof, I disliked certain faults of my own people. But I could never work up hatred for any creature on God's earth.

It was reserved for Nazi Germany to teach me the meaning of hatred. And only facts, continually repeated, could have sufficed. I have heard a good many explanations and theories as to why the Germans treated their P.O.W's as they did. (But none sufficed me, except the recognition of an unpleasant and deep-rooted potential in their character. If this were ever released, it could develop like a cancer). Why and to what purpose should they have adopted a scientific system of starving us? In my own case I was starved for over six months. Others of my friends were victimised for a period of 10-12 months. Our rations consisted of a meagre loaf of bread once a week, and a scraping of margarine and turnip jam, with watery soup and mint tea each day. The Germans had all through the war – and particularly at that early stage – an abundant supply of basic foodstuffs and even luxuries. They were also systematically looting Europe. The feeding of a few thousand British prisoners could hardly have affected their food reserves. Moreover, even then there were Red Cross parcels – and still they maintained us at only just above starvation level – but no parcels were brought to our camp. We were reduced to the most pitiful state, with scarcely enough strength to drag ourselves from our bunks to the parade-ground. The less sensitive and more resourceful did not shrink from hunting cats and rats to appease their hunger. Others learnt to collect peelings from the cookhouse, and add to their rations by re-scraping them. In one way it was a valuable experience: hitherto I had confused being hungry with missing an occasional meal, now I anxiously watched the division of a loaf with a strange, sharp keenness. Every crumb was picked up. I learnt what it means to be living on the margin of utter destitution. Sometimes a man would collapse and die. It taught me a new set of values. No longer could I feel any superiority to an unfortunate whom I had once seen scavenging food from a dustbin. We ourselves used every scrap. If values became starker and selfishness was sometimes marked, the richness of selflessness and courage and collaboration and endurance was even more noteworthy.

Dysentery, jaundice, boils and other diseases wrecked our emaciated bodies: and yet nothing seemed to have any effect on the German authorities. To crown their sadistic policy the German officer staff of our camp established their mess across the wire fence. We were given the opportunity of watching them devour their rich meals and sink foaming mugs of beer. The official German propaganda of that time and thereafter maintained that the Germans had no quarrel with the British peoples. What was the object, then, of this treatment of us P.O.W's? Whatever their intention, they succeeded in obtaining a result otherwise not easy of achievement. Normally easy-going and tolerant, they made us hate their guts. It became quite clear to me that if the Germans dared to treat us British officers in this way, the fate of others must be indescribable. (And later I had evidence of it: we had the advantage of tremendous self-confidence, and the consciousness of a powerful continuity of tradition and power to support us. But what of vanquished nations, what of their own Jewish and anti-Nazi nationals? I learnt to understand the power of this evil growth, I learnt to comprehend why the Gestapo made people quail). Then I apologised for my feelings against our popular Press: and, as one must grumble, transferred my feelings to our pre-war government.

Eventually, as a result of strong representations by the protecting power, that hell-camp was broken up. On a murky Westphalian autumn day we lurched into the new camp, which had at least the privilege of being allowed the Red Cross parcels. The camp itself was a miserable assembly of tumble-down shacks which had served as a concentration camp before our arrival. We new arrivals must have made a ghastly impression upon the old-timers, for we were scarcely settled on our bunks when a shower of food, clothing, cigarettes, and other luxuries, came down on us. The reception accorded us by our brother prisoners was something to warm and humanise our black hearts.

There was old Reuben, clucking round me and smothering me with gifts and loans. A bar of chocolate of which I refused to deprive him, was termed by him a loan. In order not to lower the prestige of his race, he declared with a twinkle, he would be satisfied with a modest rate of interest – say, a square of chocolate a day till the end of the war. It was good to have him around; but the régime he prescribed for me was very severe – he intended to get me fit. I discovered he had a flair for cooking, and a knowledge of all sorts of nursing concoctions. As he put it, 'You see, I had a similar experience in Palestine during my first year there. Unemployment, dysentery, typhus, malaria, boils, came in quick succession. And during my convalescence I did light work around the camp of our collective. I worked in the kitchen, nursed the sick, and humoured our first-born babies. So take it from me –

two spoonfuls of condensed milk . . .'

I realised his joviality was far from being engendered by his surroundings, and was all trumped up for my sake. In fact Reuben and his compatriots had felt the hand of the Nazi régime. The commandant ordered the segregation of all British officers professing the Jewish faith, since in Germany Jews were not allowed to house together with Aryans. There were seven of them who put themselves down as Jews: many took the precaution to register as Presbyterians, R.C's, etc., Reuben and his friends felt that such an overt act by the Germans was a breach of the Geneva Convention, and created a dangerous precedent of racial discrimination. On top of this, one of his pals, recaptured after an attempt to escape, was brutally maltreated and bayoneted by the German guards.

Our own petty affairs were, however, soon forgotten in the interest aroused by the stirring events of the first Russian winter – the great cold of 1941/42. That winter was also a fearful experience for us prisoners: but nothing could damp our spirits when the effect of the winter on the German armies in the East became known. We knew then that the 'good old Russkies' were not beaten, and that the Hun had met his match. During that winter, while I recovered rapidly in health, I picked up again the threads of my earlier conversations with Reuben, and made him start on the story of his life.

It began, casually enough, with random remarks about the Russian winter and the Russian character. Reuben held the Russian character in high esteem, and appeared to know a good deal about Russia, although he averred he had never been in Russia proper. He had a smattering of Russian, as of six other languages, and it was quite clear to me he had not acquired it at school.

'Oh, there is nothing unusual about it,' he began one frosty evening, 'things don't come to us by miracles. After all, when closely investigated, miracles turn out to be the most commonplace manifestations of man's mental apparatus, or of the law-abiding forces of nature. We certainly know very little about either of them, but we do know more than our fathers did. No, miracles had no part in my life. I came to know Russians and Russian because my family moved down from the area of the upper Dniester to settle on the Pruth. My father maintained that it was done for the sake of his five sons and two daughters. The town of Czernowitz, where we settled in 1907, boasted a university, colleges, banks and trading centres, and suited the educational ideals of my father admirably. My mother on the other hand, gave it as her opinion that father moved because he got fed up with the patronage of his rich father-in-law: and moreover, the small Jewish community on the wooded hills of the Dniester offered little scope for gossips and busy-bodies. I have a strong suspicion that mother was right . . . And so a small boy, dark, pale and ailing, found himself in the old Austro-Hungarian empire, not far from the Austro-Russian border.'

Reuben stopped for a moment, as his mind sorted out old scenes: 'On a late autumn day of 1914 . . .', here he paused to interpolate a remark. 'You must know that our schools had closed down a little earlier. We heard it was because our dear old Franz Josef had a quarrel with that monstrous Nicolai, the Tsar of the Russias.' 'Well,' he continued, 'on a late autumn day that boy was contemplating his day's adventures. He and his gang were in a state of war with Franek the Ukrainian boy, who threw stones at him, and fled afterwards to the protecting wings of his elder brothers – butchers and cab-drivers – husky fellows, who always enjoyed rough fun with the little Judases.* Something must be done about it, and yet there was no help from his own elder brothers, and certainly none from father. Father kept on saying that nobody ever threw stones at him, and if Franek was throwing stones at me, I must have provoked him. I had some difficulty in following the logic of my father's argument: after all I had only called Franek "pisspot", and everyone knew his trousers were always wet . . . While considering a grand strategy of retribution, I became aware of sharp reports and many black dots on the horizon. The house became alive, everyone running hither and thither and shouting out, "The cossacks, the cossacks are coming!" The dots grew bigger, and I saw a swarm of shaggy ponies, ridden by burly devils just as shaggy, rifle in one hand and sabre in the other'. (Here I interrupted Reuben, to ask him if he expected me to swallow that one). 'How did they guide their ponies?' With a surprised and pitying look he brushed aside my objection. 'They live in the saddle: their heelless boots are not even adapted to walking long distances. And naturally they have such understanding and control of their horses, that their calves are enough to direct their mounts – as is the case with any first-class riders.'

* The general term for a Jew was 'Judas' or 'Crucifier'.

'At any rate they came galloping down the rolling meadows which rose in front of our house. Bullets struck the façade, and panic-stricken Austrian soldiers tried to make a stand in the ditches and behind hedges. I still looked on, greatly excited at seeing War with a capital W. But then something happened that sent me reeling back with a hysterical outcry. A cossack's sabre came down – I can still see the glimmer of the flashing steel – and halved the torso of an Austrian soldier. The gaping parts opened wide, and fell splashing to the ground. I did not wait for more ...

'That's how the war opened for me. For four years it became my playground, and its faithful companions – death, hunger, arson, revolution – became my playmates. I knew no tin soldiers, or lifeless toys. I played on trenches and freshly dug graves. I climbed howitzers, and rode on gun-carriages. I scouted with Austrians, and fraternised with Cossacks. I swore in all languages, wandered with refugees, and marched with revolutionaries ... I did, in fact, everything a well brought up child should not do.'

Reuben stopped to light his pipe. 'I didn't think', he continued, waving it in front of me as if it were a cossack's sabre, 'that details would matter to you. But the events are too varied to relate shortly. I'll mention one or two things which left a lasting impression on me ... The Russians occupied our town three times, and were eventually driven out. On the occasion of their second breakthrough across the Pruth, father decided to send the family away. Three of my elder brothers were doing their duty in the Austrian army, and mother and my sisters lived in permanent fear of the Russians – although they did no more harm than Austrian or Bavarian troops. Father remained behind to "protect" his property: and on a winter morning we were stowed with our bundles on a sledge, and driven off in the "direction of Vienna".

'The roads could not hold the vast throng of refugees: so we spread across fields, knee-deep in snow, in order to make haste because we believed the Russians to be on our heels. I can't remember much of that day: I was miserably cold; and the wet from snow and perspiration turned to cold shivers whenever I took my turn on the sledge – for the skinny horses were not capable of dragging the whole load. But I shall never forget the fantastic ceremony performed by all the Jewish mothers – it was a Friday – to welcome the Queen of Sabbath. In every traditional Jewish household the mother of the family lights a candle on Friday evening for each member of the family. Jewish mothers

33

had kept up the tradition through the ages, and they were not going to fail now. We children were handed the candles and it was our task to mould the candle-holders from the soft snow and plant the candles therein. Within a few moments a flickering sea of light, stretching from horizon to horizon, announced the entry of the Queen of Sabbath. There must have been hundreds and hundreds of Jewish families on the road to Vienna. Mother told me to say the prayer, and I sang the lovely tune of "Come, O Come! Queen of the Sabbath!" We moved on, but I couldn't refrain from looking back at the little flames as they bravely fought the snowflakes in the icy embrace of their chandeliers.

'Soon enough we came out of our painfully intense fantasies of revelry, rich food and white tablecloth, carp in onions, golden chicken-broth, evoked so vividly by the rite of the candles. On arrival in a little village where we intended to stop for the night, a ghastly spectacle awaited us. In front of the hostelry we came upon a young mother with the most tragically lovely features I have ever seen. She was holding an empty cushion-wrapping in her arms, and oblivious to all except her grief, was lamenting the loss of her first, and only, baby. Her child must have slipped out of the wrapping when the mother was traversing one of the lonely forest paths: it probably passed into a coma, folded in the soft snow, before the icy cold stole its last flickering breath. Only on her arrival, as she uncovered her breast to feed it as of yore, did she become aware of her fearful, irreplaceable loss . . .' (Here Reuben paused, and I did not break into his memories. Then he turned to me with twitching lips): 'Since then, Jack, I feel terribly blasé when tragedies are enacted on the stage. Medea, Sappho, Macbeth, and even Gorki's "Mother", which I have seen in later life performed by the best tragedians of my time, all of these appeared insipid and anæmic when compared to the bitter lament of the young mother pressing that empty cushion to her naked breast. Under the circumstances no search was possible. The mother was finally led inside the house, to whimper through the night.

'That first day was also for us the last of our flight. Next morning mother was down with pneumonia, and in a few days' time the Cossacks from whom we had fled, were to enter the village. When mother was out of danger, I, aged ten, as the only male of the family, went round to see the local Russian commandant to ask for a passport to return to our place. In a mixture of broken Ukrainian and Russian I tremblingly stuttered my request.

I must have expected to be thrown out, or whipped with the Cossack knout, or made to suffer any of the infinite variety of atrocities ascribed to the barbarians by Austrian propaganda. I was therefore completely taken by surprise when the old war-horse got up from his rickety chair and gave me a smothering hug. He promised not only a passport, but also a good sledge – he knew what the local peasants were like – and one Cossack as escort, in order that none of those "crawling vermin of infantrymen" should dare to molest my dear *matushka*. He was as good as his word; and our progress home was undisturbed, even if we had to break our journey very often. This was to enable our escort to combat a dangerous chill he felt creeping into his bones: his medicine seemed to be available in every pub we passed. So we arrived home in state; and our Cossack, pocketing a generous tip, withdrew with a hearty assurance that although the Jews had crucified Jesus Christ, they were a generous and kindly lot. But the sight that met us inside our house needed no explanation. All the rooms were stripped bare, except for a few pieces of old furniture. Father's stately beard, blue-black before we left, had visible silver streaks; he looked and was a broken man. All he could manage to utter was that the plunder was not the work of Russian soldiers, but of our own Ukrainian and Polish neighbours and dependants. On the Austrian evacuation of Czernowitz, father had withdrawn a large sum of money and kept it in a safe. That also, had gone. Mother was still ill, with feverish pink roses showing on the protruding cheekbones of her haggard face. But she let that face meet the fortunes of the world undaunted. "Father and children," she addressed us, "what is all this worry about old junk and money? At least we are all alive. Let us pray that my three sons in the army may come back to us in good health. The Lord gave, and the Lord hath taken away; blessed be the name of the Lord. Amen". It was the longest speech I had ever heard her make. She must have known that much more was in store for us, because in a few months' time she departed from us."

Reuben's pipe had been out for some time, but he still used it to emphasize various remarks. 'You can see now why I know something of Russians and war? Such apocalyptic playgrounds, and they well merit the name, were a right and fitting environment for Jewish kids everywhere east of the Rhine. Otherwise we might have grown up with a false conception of our destiny, as many of my generation, in spite of it, unfortunately did. And believe me, they paid dearly for living a life governed by false pretences and sham.'

The dying flicker of the carbide lamp brought his talk to an end. I left Reuben fussing about with his blankets, and walked over the crisp and hard-trodden snow to my shack. A refrain of Russian winters kept weaving itself with the destiny of peoples and individuals in my mind, an insistent rhythm of thought which resounded in my mind as I lay dozing on my bunk, until it passed into the deep sleep of winter night.

CHAPTER THREE

FLAGS IN THE BREEZE

IN THE 'BAG' we followed the events of the war far more intensely than most people outside; and our military alliance and twenty years' treaty with Russia became in due course the most hotly debated topic. A British officers' camp has naturally a certain political atmosphere of its own; but war, and the clear criticism which prison can evoke, had made deep inroads into many pre-war unthought-out views and sentiments. Little natural sympathy for communist Russia could be expected amongst the class from which the majority of us were recruited. Yet, although many dismissed the matter as war-time expediency, the vast majority felt the matter could hardly rest there. Russia, as a clever young lawyer put it, was not merely a state but an armed doctrine; and a victorious Russia meant further territorial acquisition for the doctrine; even if Russia as such abstained from purely imperial aggrandisement. Yet people could not be blind to the advance Russia had made in the past twenty-five years, and the inner enthusiasm which alone could have held them in the early part of the war; the advance had been in spite of civil war, famine, and foreign obstruction. Russia was now a powerful state. It is dangerous to criticise from a deep-seated antagonism to communism if one has no idea of the reality – and I began to have some respect for the effects of that reality – to do so is to waste one's antagonism on one's own fantasy, which may have little more connection with the actual than its name. I decided to investigate the matter, and collected together a group of people who knew of European problems largely from first-hand experience or who were otherwise competent.

It would be tedious to follow our investigations, but they were inspiring. I had read history at Cambridge, and covered much old ground: but everything became alive. At school, history had been dates and incidents – Alfred and his cakes, or Raleigh and his cloak. I learnt that the break with Rome was precipitated by the obstruction to Henry VIII's divorce from Catherine, and that the British Empire grew by a series of happy incidents. At the university I learnt more to appreciate the true flow of continuity, the dynamics of events and personalities. But in a way, history became abstract and impersonal. I might study the French revolution, but really such things were not for me – it was objective and unreal, in the sense that I could not subjectively experience it. This applied to wars and civil wars, famine, migrations, and to the play of economics – the oil and financial struggles. Interspersed were new and half-disconnected fragments, the gout of a statesman, or the glands of kings and queens, the medicaments of history.

The discussions in the camp helped to make history real for me. They also removed much unconsidered prejudice, and made me I hope, more tolerant. Revolutions no longer shocked me, crusades no longer elevated me – they both might play a part in life. If we made of Cromwell the regicide a national hero, could I deny the same tribute to Lenin? If I do not accept communism as a final or complete or even necessary answer to human destiny, at least I have learnt to appreciate more clearly its aim. In our own lax era before this war I could hardly find any moral or material excuse for the excommunication of social rebels. Whether the rebels be Nazarenes, Jacobins or Suffragettes, they are apt to become accepted in time, and their contribution gratefully acknowledged. Russia claims to have found an economic solution – politically she has no final answer except democracy – and in so doing naturally challenges any tendency of ours to inertia. We admit that the purely individualistic age has exhausted itself – it was probably necessary for early expansion in the dawn of the machine age – but now we have entered on a period of scientific planning. The problem after the war will be to find the way to a synthesis uniting equality of opportunity with planning, and yet not to lose vital personal liberty. Our group felt that a Russo-British alliance was a necessary pre-requisite for the realisation of such a synthesis, as for the maintenance of world peace.

The study and exchange of views on these and related matters brought out yet another chapter in Reuben's life. He was, of course, an active member of our group, although a bit reserved and non-committal at times. I did not believe that his occasional reticence was prompted by modesty, since he was as cocksure of himself and his way of life as a cartoon of John Bull in the 'nineties.

I cornered him one morning, when he dropped in for a mug of cocoa, and I soon realised that, as usual, he rather enjoyed these discussions. He settled down in the one and only comfortable chair in the room, and motioned me on to my bunk.

'You are looking far too eager for my liking', he opened up. 'A gentleman should always appear bored – even when he makes love . . . By the way, you make a good cup of cocoa, but I should like a bit more sugar. Thank you, that's better. And what about one of your Egyptian cigarettes? Ah, there they are . . . You've asked a straight question, and there is no dodging it.'

'The topics we have discussed recently are, to my way of thinking, not of an abstract and scientific nature. It happens that we know less about man than about a tadpole. The reason for it is quite evident, if deplorable. When an individual or a group has to decide on a course of action, there is little objective matter at their disposal, in particular when we discuss social and economic planning, and above all, principles of social morality. Exchange of views and an earnest investigation are highly desirable, but in these matters, what we think is not so important as what we do. I was very pleased to hear your own views, and I think they might come to fruition, provided you, and all those who think as you do begin to live up to them. Some people measure idealism in terms of faith in the godlike essence of man: as for myself, I prefer the idealist to idealism; the man who lives ideally to the many who talk idealism. There is a marked difference between the difficulty of to-day and the difficulties of a generation ago. From one point of view it was easier for my generation: for, before we came to elaborate programmes for others, we had to save our own bodies and souls from utter ruin. We simply set out to do things on the basis of using mere crumbs of principles, and left the worry about plans and programmes for the future. Your circle has done good work on plans and programmes: but I am afraid that the gentlemen concerned did not bother much about what they, personally, are called upon to do. This is not necessarily a criticism of them, nor have I any doubts as to their honesty. It is merely a general symptom of our civilization, and of the turn our political life has taken. People have ceased to believe that for the realisation of a higher morality – call it Christianity or Socialism or any name you like – their lives must be rearranged accordingly. That is a severe and, I am afraid, an out-of-date point of view. I don't mind if you call me an Utopian, but I believe that most of the movements – such as prophetic Judaism, Christianity, and Western socialism – have failed, because those who preached them were larger in number than those who lived them.

Do not postpone your efforts until after conditions have changed, but do your utmost in order to bring about the apposite conditions. The traditional wrangle about what comes first, new conditions or a new way of life reminds me of the debate: security first – disarmament first. I believe they must be one organic and indivisible whole, if things are ever to change without violent convulsions. As it is, man's progress has come about as much by violent revolutions as by slow biological growth. Nobody can deny that revolutions have cut many knots in history, which a steady rational handling might have been unable to disentangle. I have a deep sympathy with those who deplore the immense waste of life and goods caused by revolutionary upheavals: but we should not forget that the destruction and waste brought about by decades and sometimes centuries, of evolutionary experiments, exceeds by far those wrought by one violent short cut. Both wars and revolutions could have been avoided if man were not a rational animal – the worst possible combination in the whole creation. Either animal or rational, yes. But a mixture . . .!!

I myself am a child of revolution. If war was the playground, then revolution set the pace and directions of the youth of my generation. Revolutions – and I am entitled to use the plural – were probably the most breath-taking experiences of our lives. They caused us suffering enough, but they also cleared the path for a new, and in our own modest way, a revolutionary beginning.

Personally I am indebted to these revolutions for two things. Through them I met Anton Josip Bogdanoff; and by them I found a way through smothering and incompatible false loyalties.

My meeting with Bogdanoff was terrifying; later knowing him became sheer joyous adventure. It happened on the second day of the Russian revolution in 1917. The Russian garrison in our town made the most of it. Having disposed of some of their generals and officers, who refused to acknowledge the new government in Moscow, the whole garrison and population of the town gave themselves up to revelry and feasting. Red flags and national flags, probably of all nations in the world, brass bands, demonstrations, speeches, folk-dances, much hugging and kissing, fraternisation between civilians and soldiers – such were the outward means of expressing the fervour of the revolution.

There was no violence, and perfect order was maintained by the revolutionary committee of soldiers and civilians who took charge of all affairs. We civilians had every reason to rejoice, since the first act of the Revolution in our town was to release the hundred hostages kept in prison by the commandant of the town as guarantee for the good behaviour of the civilians, and the suspension of the heavy monetary tribute imposed on us. The liberated hostages – the majority of them Jews – were led in procession to their houses, where more speeches and feasting followed. We boys had it all our own way, being carried on soldiers' backs, borne on decorated trucks, and generally petted and spoilt by all and sundry. Had it not been for my meeting with Bogdanoff, that would probably have been the picture of a revolution left in my mind. Who was Bogdanoff, you ask? Listen.

On the second night of those hectic days, our family sat inside the teashop kept by my sister during the various Russian occupations. The shutters and the door were locked, and I suppose we entertained ourselves by exchanging experiences of the day's celebrations. Our cheerful chatter, however, was abruptly silenced by sharp knocks at the door. It was a late hour for any caller, and we felt rather frightened. As no reply came from within, the rappings grew more impatient, and finally father got up, went to the door and asked: 'Who is there?' 'Bogdanoff is here, will you open the door!' There was nothing for it but to open, although the name Bogdanoff meant nothing to us. No sooner was the door open than the apparition – the apparition of Schlüsselburg as we called him later – stood on the threshold of the shop. There he stood, a giant of a man – or a ghost – we couldn't say which. He was clad in the usual black leather coat and cap of a Russian driver. All his extremities, from ear to toe were twitching violently. In one of his trembling hands he held a pistol the size of a carbine. He had sharply protruding cheek-bones and huge ears twitching angrily. He looked the picture of Nemesis. I quickly took up a position behind my elder sister – I had no confidence in father as far as militant affairs were concerned – for sister Ethel was our 'Cossack' (a nickname bestowed on her after she had slapped the face of a Russian who made some lurid remarks about feminine graces in her presence). On occasions she even knew how to bring me to heel: reason enough for me to respect her. The apparition seemed satisfied with what he saw, for he threw cap and pistol on the table and addressed us thus:

'Brothers and sisters! To-day we celebrate the first revolution. It won't be the last. I had a busy day watching and directing the revolution, and now I am hungry. Let us sit down and Matushka will bring us some tea'. It was not a speech but a series of explosions, as each sentence was spat out, and was followed by a violent rocking of shoulders and twitching of ears. Everybody obeyed his command, except Ethel, who sped to the kitchen, thus exposing me to the surprised scrutiny of our guest. 'Ha, a boy, I love malcziks. Come here, don't be shy, I am only a stupid lump of a man', he gurgled. My eyes were on the pistol. 'Oh, excuse me, I forgot about that rod'. He picked up the rod as if it were a toothpick, and slipped it into a pocket of his leather coat. Well, there was nothing for it but to go up to him. He picked me up and seated me gently – the shock of that gentle touch from a ghost – on a chair next to him. That evening he told us his story. Next day he drove me in his car 'to watch over the revolution', and he even allowed me to laugh at his horse ears because, as he used to admonish me, 'better the ears of a horse, than the brain of a donkey' – pointing slyly at his ears and at my skull. We became fast friends – Anton and I – although he gave me the creeps occasionally.

Bogdanoff – Anton Yosip – was about thirty years old and a skilled mechanic, when he was sentenced to ten years' imprisonment in the dungeons of the Schlüsselburg fortress, for taking part in that 'great treachery of 1905'. He had spent about five years there when he went mad, and attempted suicide by hanging himself to the bars of his cell; he regained consciousness in the padded cell of an asylum. Anton could not remember having been violent, but his warder – a friend of his, smuggled in by the revolutionary organization – attested to his violence by a demonstration of bruises and black spots on his body. They managed to get him pardoned and he recovered quickly; but his nervous spasms – they would go with him to his grave, 'and wouldn't St. Peter chuckle at my horse-ears, as you, little scoundrel, do'. He never returned to the Putilov works in Petersburg, but became a professional revolutionary. His job was mainly to lay up stores of arms, to manufacture bombs, and assist occasionally 'in their disposal'. Just before the outbreak of the war he became convinced that terrorist activities were not his line, and were not the means to bring about the revolution. He joined the Bolsheviki, who were opposed to terrorist activities, and worked for the organization of the masses and the intellectuals as the potential army which would strike the blow when the time was ripe. At the outbreak of the war he was conscripted and given the task by his party of organising 'soviets' in the army. 'That dunderhead of a Kerensky thinks that he made the revolution. We shall see, my boy. Only the Bolshevik can save Russia, and, *ya bogo* (by God), they will'. That is one side of Bogdanoff: the other Bogdanoff was revealed to me in his talks.

I cannot after so many years recall the full character of our conversations . . . I mean my silly childish questions and his answers. It must have been a sight, that tower of a man, who had no children of his own, and had never talked to children about such topics as revolution, economics, Marxism, religion and so forth, straining all his faculties to make me understand, or at least feel, what he was talking about. No learned pedagogue or leader in our youth movement had ever done it better than Anton. Just to show you the man he was, I will try to reconstruct such a talk:

Boy: Anton, what is a revolution?

Anton (looking down at the boy to ascertain whether he is in earnest): Revolution is a movement. Compare the life of a community to a wheel, which is kept spinning. Whenever that wheel stops spinning or slows down because let's say, somebody puts a spoke in its way, then men must be found to give it a new violent push to keep it going. That violent push is called revolution.

Boy: Who puts spokes into the wheel?

Anton: Who? Greed, cruelty, ignorance, fatheads, Czars, policemen, priests, rabbis, teachers – *o Bogo* – there is no end to my list of evils.

Boy: Who are the men who give the wheel a violent push?

Anton: Boy, you'll be the death of me yet. Is there no God in your heart, that you torture me? (*Boy smiles blissfully, knowing well that this sort of outburst will produce the choicest results*). Who would start such a revolution? Men would start it – men hungry for bread and freedom, and men hungry – well hungry for God – for beauty, goodness, joy, for children's laughter. Ever heard what Moses did to the Egyptian slave-driver? He killed him and started a revolution. Ever heard what Jesus did to the moneylenders in the temple? He drove them out . . . Ever heard of Spartacus . . . ? 'and out came a string of names, strange, and unknown to me. A whole galaxy of saints, martyrs, social and national revolutionaries, finishing up with Lenin.'

Boy: What is a *burjui* (bourgeois)? The people were shouting at the demonstration, 'Down with the *burjuis!*' – What is it?

Anton: What a boy for questions, and who am I to reply? (*Boy crestfallen*): All right, all right, I'll talk, even if it kills me. A *burjui* is a man who takes away 50 roubles and gives you back 20.

Boy: Don't be silly, Anton Josip. (*Red horse-ears twitch violently*). Who would give a man 50 roubles to get back 20?

Anton (rocking): No, you wouldn't, you imp – Oh yes you would. If you were hungry and must work you would. At present you either work for others – and get back only a fraction of what you earn – or you make others work for you, and cash in on the balance which they deserve and never get.

Boy: Why, that's silly, why not work for ourselves and share everything we make?

Anton (lifting the boy to heaven): Yes, that's what Lenin must bring about again, because Moses and Jesus and Buddha have been betrayed by evil men. It must be done all over again.

Boy: But . . .

Anton: Oh, no! I still want to live to see the revolution finished, and you are not to kill me. My throat is dry like the Sahara, and there is not a drop of liquid in my flask. Now you run along, otherwise Ethel (he also was in awe of my sister) will throw me out when I come next for her heavenly cakes.

'Well, it is a poor attempt, but I wish I could convey to you the deep religious simplicity of that giant, and the way humility and revolutionary drive were blended into one in that vigorous being. You will understand now why I had no difficulty in understanding the events in Russia, and why I have faith in Russia. Well, I think we'll call it a day', said Reuben.

But I still wanted to hear what he meant by his release from incompatible – while false – loyalties, as he put it.

'That's easy enough, and quickly told', Reuben replied, while hanging on to the door handle. 'But as Bogdanoff said, my throat is dry like the Sahara, and I may add, my stomach is empty. We have still got a few years of enforced comradeship, so what's the hurry?'

CHAPTER FOUR

CHAINS THAT DO NOT FETTER

WE WERE GLAD to exchange Westphalia for a camp in Bavaria. The drab and monotonous landscape of Westphalia and the sordid accommodation the camp afforded would have been too much for us altogether, had it not been for the fun we derived from large-scale escaping activities, to which the place lent itself admirably.

Tunnelling in the loamy and sandy soil was relatively easy, provided one had an adequate supply of timber for props. The wooden shacks, and particularly the rafters of the roof constructions supplied our needs. We very soon came to the conclusion that too much wood was wasted on roof construction, and that they would hold up with less than orthodox stress-calculations seemed to demand. The digging of a tunnel was nevertheless no mean engineering feat. Distances to be covered were considerable – anything between forty and a hundred and twenty yards; water had to be pumped out, light and ventilation provided for, the excavated soil disposed of, the German security staff misled: so in all there were interesting and remarkable tasks for organisers, technicians, engineers and security chaps. Pumps, elevators, ventilators, baby trains and railway lines, lighting installations, tools and many more items had to be made of the only available raw material – Red Cross tins and odds and ends stolen from the Germans.

The Germans found the results of our ingenuity so amazing, that as soon as they had captured a fair selection of our implements they opened an exhibition in the town under the propaganda heading. 'What tins can be used for'. The R.A.F. officers in our camp were, of course, in the van of all escaping activities. In the course of six or eight months about fifty tunnels had been completed, and when we eventually left the place, the German authorities charged us a fantastic sum for damages, for as they argued – and we heartily agreed – the place was unfit for further habitation. The huts had their foundations undermined, and the roofs had no struts to support them. They firmly expected that a good-sized gale would bring the whole structure toppling to the ground.

45

As long as these activities lasted, the German security officer Hauptmann Rademacher, a rowdy ill-mannered brute, and his numerous staff could scarcely cope with the filling in of discovered or abandoned tunnels; and they were quite unable to interfere seriously with the burrowing craze. Many escaped, though naturally only a few eventually got home.

The most daring and dazzling attempt to escape was nevertheless reserved not for diggers but for a scaling party. Major X conceived the plan, probably suggested to him by a passage in the history of the Peninsular War. The party of about sixty officers went through a regular training, lasting for several months. Collapsible ladders for negotiating the wire fence were constructed and tested in numerous dress-rehearsals – and yet absolute security was preserved. At zero hour of the night in question, the operation was opened by fusing the lights on the perimeter. Next came a feint attack, which, as foreseen, attracted the attention of sentries and prowlers already confused by the failure of the lights. While sentries and alarmed German reinforcements dealt with the feint, the main operation unfolded, dead on time. Over the scaling ladders about thirty officers crossed into freedom before the Germans realised what was happening. In the morning, the inmates of the camp and the Germans viewed the ladders, and a note posted by the escapers. It said:

ONE MORE SUCCESSFUL BRITISH EVACUATION.

Thus we said '*Auf nimmer Wiedersehen*' to Warburg in Westphalia. Our new camp, at Eichstätt in Bavaria, presented a pleasant contrast to Westphalia. At our feet ran the sluggish waters of the Altmühl, and surrounding us were hill, forest and meadow. The Germans, however, took good care that we should not take advantage of our new surroundings. Flushed with victory over the 'Dieppe invasion', and still unconscious of the consequences of their steam-roller drive to the Volga and Caucasus, they felt that the time was propitious for striking a blow against the undaunted spirit of their British captives. Where their former policy of starvation, bullying, pestilential accommodation, and cattle-truck journeys had failed, handcuffs and chains, they fancied, would at last succeed. The galling English superiority would be overcome. A flimsy and hypocritical pretext was at hand. Had not the British, during their commando raids, and at Dieppe, tied the hands of German prisoners until they arrived safely on board ship? An expediency measure lasting

15 – 30 minutes – the Germans admitted it to be such – which saved the life of many a German prisoner was proclaimed an insult to the honour of the German nation. The Führer in person ordered 'retaliation'. All prisoners taken at Dieppe were to be put in handcuffs for an indefinite period unless the British government apologized for the barbarous deeds of its subordinates, and unless it gave adequate guarantees for the future. When the British government put an equal number of German prisoners in handcuffs, the Germans trebled the number and by simple bad luck, I was among those honoured with a pair of brand-new Gestapo bracelets.

The German commandant of our camp – a stumpy peacock of a man, with rolls of flesh on the back of his neck – probably hoped that the British prisoners would reply to the German measure with a mutiny. He had machine guns posted round us, with specially selected trustworthy firing squads, when the interpreter read out: 'Ze order of ze German high command'. Instead of mutiny, the astounded commandant and his henchmen found themselves assailed by roaring cheers and derision. The situation thus created was, of course, not foreseen by the Germans: and machine guns were rather out of place against English madmen who laughed when you put humiliating steel bracelets on their wrists. The indolent British had them again: even chains – created for slaves and criminals – failed to humiliate them. While we made a dazzling mockery of Nazi 'kultur' the German officers and men slunk back to their quarters, somewhat puzzled as to who had been most humiliated by the incident.

The moral victory was ours, but so were the handcuffs, and they were far from amusing. They remained with us for 14 months. For two months we had police handcuffs, tying wrist to wrist. They were replaced by handcuffs with a 40 cm. chain in between, allowing some freedom of movement for our arms. For six months we were isolated from the remainder of the camp, and under permanent observation of special sentries posted in our quarters. Any officers found with his chains off, had his wrists roped behind his back for seven days. After six months the German attitude relaxed, the isolation was lifted, and from then onwards the matter became a farce; we must still parade with our chains on for morning and evening check-ups, but during the remainder of the day the Germans ceased to bother. From then onwards chains could be found hung up in cupboards, or even in the lost property office. Occasional German raids and subsequent punishments no longer had any effect. However, it took the German higher command 14 months to put an official end to this outrage.

Reuben and his compatriots were, of course – by special order – among those fettered. Reuben enjoyed the manner in which we reacted to the German measure, though he had a few words for the Germans whenever the cold steel stung his rheumatic wrists. He was in high glee about the development of the war, and summed up the German position at the end of the second Russian winter in one pithy sentence: 'The first Russian winter froze the Germans stiff, the second melted them in the furnaces of Stalingrad, Tunis and Hamburg.'

I was anxious to go on with our talks, and then the matter was brought up by Reuben himself. One day with our chains dangling, he asked me whether I had ever been in chains before. I looked at him sharply and asked him what he meant. I had had little opportunity for committing burglary or murder as yet, I said: and anyway, what was he driving at?

'Well', he replied, 'it isn't only murder that fetters your wrists – and what's more, your whole being. I had my hands chained once in Rumania, not for murder, but for assisting Jewish lads to escape from Russia to Rumania on their way to Palestine. A Rumanian gendarme found me nosing round at Tighina on the lower Dniester, and my turn-out must have suggested to him that I was a Russian spy.

It was one of those Russian winters with the frozen Dniester providing a good bridge across, making it difficult for both Russian and Rumanian sentries to guard the whole stretch; particularly as we had the assistance of Rumanian C.I.D. men – for good money. Nevertheless many a young and promising life had its blood mingled with the ice of the Dniester. I once saw such a red hole in the ice, burned by the hot, pulsating, life-blood of one of our boys. The Rumanians kept me in chains and in a filthy prison for 24 hours. I had interesting companions there in the shape of unlicensed whores, bandits, and sundry respectable citizens. The Rumanian chief of police had nothing to charge me with, but still a fat bribe had to be paid before I got out of that rotten place.

'I saw chains on one other occasion – no, by a sheer fluke of circumstances, not on my own wrists – but on the hands of some

of my best friends. It was in Palestine. My friends were caught –
unforgivable blunder! – training for the defence of our settlements. It was during the Arab riots. I saw them dragged in chains
to Acre's historic fortress.'

I knew from my own personal experience the case Reuben referred to. Did Reuben know that I had had some responsibility
for the (of course, perfectly judicial) arrest of his friends? If he
did he gave no indication, for he continued quietly in a very
restrained voice:

'But after all what do chains of steel matter? They are painful
and sometimes even humiliating – yes, humiliating when men
whom you had good reason to regard as your friends and allies
slip them on you – however, they cannot fetter your spirit or your
faith. I found the other type of chains more embarrassing: the
transcendental chains, forged by mental stagnation and blind
surrender to historic fate; and believe me, it takes more than a
nail-file to get rid of those!

'I doubt whether you will be able to follow and understand
what I mean by that much-abused metaphor. No free man, born
into his own world, where nation, state and blood relations blend
into one, can have a notion of the crazy entanglements in which
a boy of my generation found himself. I myself, who lived
through the same stages as they, cannot comprehend how my
ancestors and most of my contemporaries managed to face up to
it. I should have thought that even the sharpest dose of cynicism
and hypocrisy would not enable a man to survive such conflicting
forces. You wonder Jack, what I am getting at? Well, try to
follow me if you possible can.

'My ancestors were born, and lived all their lives among Poles
and Ukrainians, all of them subjects of the Austro-Hungarian
empire. In one sentence you notice already the tangle of four
races. Worse to come, neither Pole nor Ukrainian ever recognised
the Austrian overlord. The Poles expected my great-grandparents
to conform to a Polish patriotism: my family having come to
Poland probably in the time of Casimir the Great. The Poles
maintained – with some justification one must admit – that prior
to the unfortunate partitions of their country, my ancestors were
Polish subjects. Consequently they insisted – and Poles know how
to insist – that their descendants should declare themselves Polish
patriots; that is, declare themselves anti-Austrian, anti-Ukrainian,
and many more anti's of that nature.

49

'The Ukrainians, on the other hand – later immigrants into the Galician highlands, where they formed compact majorities – worked and fought for an independent Ukraine, stretching from the Carpathians to the Dnieper and beyond. The Ukrainian nationalists urged my grandfathers to embrace their political aims, since they, the Jews, a small minority, enjoyed the hospitality of the Ukrainian majority. To endorse the Ukrainian claim involved, of course, many more anti's: anti-Pole, anti-Austrian, and so on.

'The third partner, the actual lord of the domain, the Austrian aristocracy and bureaucracy, expected from the Jews – who were by nature neither Poles nor Ukrainians – support for the Austrian hegemony against their rebellious subjects, the Poles and Ukrainians.

'That is the stage on which my forbears had to play their part. The Jews accepted the *de facto* rule of the Austrians, but there were still considerable sections of them who considered the *demoralibus* position as well. Consequently, some of them joined up with the Polish patriots, and others with the Greater Ukrainians. The net outcome of that tragic or ludicrous state of affairs – it depends how you look upon it – was the unanimous animosity of Austrians, Poles and Ukrainians against my grandfathers and their contemporaries. They were accused by everyone in turn of being treacherous, ungrateful – in short, true to their Judas tradition. As was only natural, the Jews were at loggerheads among themselves; there were philo-Austrians, philo-Poles, and so on: and, of course, the welter in between which cared for neither. To make the picture complete, I should not omit to mention the new party which came into being at the time when my father was still a pupil at the rabbinical seminary – the Social Democrats.

'These condemned all nationalistic movements, and the "divide et impera" policy of the Austrians into the bargain. The S.D. programme had naturally many attractions for Jewish youth and the masses of poor Jews: and moreover it offered a comfortable way out of the dilemma. More fuel was added to the dissensions among the Jews themselves, and more reason for Austrians, Poles and Ukrainians to join forces in the cry that the Jews were not only lacking in loyalty, but that they were also dangerous revolutionaries and conspirators.

'You see the trap, don't you, Jack? It didn't matter what my grandfathers did – they could not do right. They were enmeshed in a hopeless tangle of divided loyalties, in which there was no place for their most elementary and incontestable loyalty – that to their own people.

'That was the world my generation was born into: but worse was to come for us in our own lifetime.

'When, in 1918, the Austrian empire collapsed, chaos came to reign supreme in all its former domains. Some called that chaos by the proud name of Revolution: but whereas the Russian revolution was for me an experience of joy and hope, an experience of Bogdanoff; the revolution sweeping over the outer fringes of the Austro-Hungarian empire was its antithesis. It was to me no triumph of an idea, but senseless dismal confusion and lawlessness. Under cover of that chaos, looting guerilla bands marched to and fro. Czernowitz and its surroundings became a no-man's land, over which Polish, Ukrainian, Rumanian and cosmopolitan bands fought their "patriotic" battles. Arson, murder and loot, particularly severe in the Jewish quarters, were the order of the day. The citizens organised a militia – wasn't I proud to see my father shouldering a rifle (I am afraid he never loaded it) – but they were not a match for the skilled ex-soldier guerilla bands.

'Eventually the Poles seized control of the city, and hoisted the flag of the Polish republic. My harassed father submitted to the inevitable, and a home-made Polish flag fluttered dismally from the roof of our house. A few schools were soon opened, and my good elders, anxious to give me some education after four years of running wild, packed me off to the Polish school. All the teachers were Poles, or Jews simulating Polish patriotism, and my tongue had to be broken in to the Polish mass concentrations of consonants, such as *prsz*.

'One morning I woke to the noise of a lively fusillade. In due course a company of armed men, with the Ukrainian colours on their armbands, marched by, and declared that we were now "liberated from the Polish yoke". Off went my sisters to collect blue, red and white rags; and out came the Ukrainian flag. We settled down under an Ukrainian régime, a new oath was taken, and then there was school again for me. The same old dilapidated building, which had seen Austrian, Russian and Polish headmasters and canes, had now to make the acquaintance of the Ukrainian species. Now the language was Ukrainian, but before I had mastered the Greek script and the Ukrainian anthem, the régime collapsed as suddenly as it had come. Versailles had spoken in the meantime, and rewarded the Rumanians for services rendered by giving them the country east and west of the Pruth. In the town and in the province there was only a small Rumanian minority – but after all, what nation had a clear majority in that blessed borderland? The Rumanians delayed their entry into the city, and the disbanded soldiery had it their own way once again.

'At last a Rumanian envoy, all gold braid, turned up in the town hall, and delivered himself of a speech to the effect that the valiant Rumanian army was ready to enter the city and establish, order – but his troops had no boots! Rumanian soldiers normally wore peasant moccasins; but Czernowitz, having seen the glory of the Austrian Imperial army, could not be humiliated by receiving bootless soldiers. The citizens were promptly ordered to deliver all army boots, or any other kind of footgear, to the Rumanian commissariat. Then we had the pleasure of seeing the Rumanian army limp into town. The poor peasants in uniform must have suffered agony; no sooner were their arms piled than they divested themselves of their boots – an invention of the devil, so they classed them – revealing dirty blistered feet, since their Q.M. had omitted to impose on the citizens a tribute of socks as well.

Now the inevitable order to hoist the red, yellow and blue stripes of the Rumanian flag! My sisters, by now expert flag-makers, replaced the white strip of the Ukrainian flag with a yellow strip from an old dress, and out went the symbol of our loyalty to the King of All the Rumanians. The Rumanian masters lost no time in "nationalising" our life. There were not enough Rumanians in town for all the jobs, so Rumanians had to be imported. I went again to the same old school, and now the Rumanian language came to blot out all my former linguistic flights. The first few days at school were very pleasant, as all our "study" was made up of rehearsals of the anthem (same tune and words as in God Save The King), and making of flags for the reception of some Rumanian General expected in the town, and similar patriotic duties.

'That is, as you see, my first-hand study of constitutions, national states, anthems, flags, and ever-changing loyalties. I suppose some of my relations, who stuck stubbornly to Czernowitz, had to go through a similar course of the political sciences during the present war.

'Now remember, Jack,' Reuben continued, after having assured himself that I had managed somehow to get a notion of that political jig-saw puzzle, 'I was then only thirteen years old: but war and revolutions are implacable taskmasters. I already had my own sentiments and perhaps even views on things: but I could not unravel the political philosophy of my father. One day, when I could not bear it any longer, I approached him and asked for an explanation.

"Father, what are you? I mean, whose subject are you, which of all those flags you have hoisted in your lifetime is actually yours? I know you were an Austrian patriot, and that you even encouraged one of your sons to go and volunteer for the front before he need have done. But now the whole family has been turned into a shop for the manufacture of flags. As a town councillor you have also sworn allegiance to God knows how many national republics. You can't expect me to do the same!" I cried in exasperation. Father was rather sad, but not unprepared for my attack, because he himself must have felt the tragedy of it all. He was very candid with me.

'"Don't you know, Reuben, what I am? I am a Jew, and nothing but a Jew, and so are you. As such, I don't count amongst those who struggle to have their flag flying from the tower of the municipality. Nobody ever asked me, or is likely to do so in the future, whom and what I prefer. Who am I to say to whom Czernowitz belongs? I have grown up under Austrian rule, and naturally fulfilled all my duties punctiliously. That is finished: what else remains for me or for you, but to take orders from those who have the power to enforce them? Do you expect me to hoist the blue and white flag? The game of politics is not for us my son – we should be content to make a living when we can, and pray that our life and property may be protected."

'That about sums up my father's political philosophy at the time. Well, Jack, father's attitude was one of the things that started my generation on the way of rebellion. We came to realise that our fathers were in bondage, and although aware of it, they either lacked the courage or the strength of character to free themselves. In fact they failed to see – as many still fail – that there was an alternative to their miserable slavery.'

So far I had left Reuben to go on with his tale, without interrupting him. But at this point I felt a deep sympathy with his father's plight, and little sympathy with his own predicament.

What could his father do under the circumstances, and what, for that matter, had Reuben to suggest? I said as much to Reuben.

'There was, and still is, of course, an alternative', insisted Reuben. 'As you probably noticed, my father asked me whether I expected him to hoist the blue and white flag. Father knew by that time that I had come to regard the flag of Zionism as our own flag, the Jewish flag, and as the symbol of what I actually expected him to do – to pack himself and the whole family off to Palestine. It meant cutting the knot, and he was as yet not prepared to do it.

'My own conversion to Zionism was the outcome of an exhilarating incident, which, had it not occurred during the Russian revolution of 1917, would surely have happened to me at some later stage. There could be no question for me of sitting down under my father's fatalistic political philosophy. I was not going to discard flags like so many handkerchiefs. I was all set for an answer compatible with the one and only loyalty I was aware of – the loyalty to my own race. The synagogue made no appeal to me. My young impetuous soul was longing for an elementary answer to the pride in my own blood. There must be such an answer, and if there were not, it had to be created. When I saw therefore, on the first morning of the 1917 revolution a soldiers' truck, decorated with blue-white flags, and with slogans written in Hebrew characters, I embraced it instantly as the answer to my tortured pride. The slogans were simple – too simple – as I came to realise later –

"The Jews will return to Erez Israel" –

"Balfour Declaration for a Jewish State in Palestine" –

"The Jews will yet become as one of the peoples" –

"Long live the tiller of the soil in the Holy Land."

'I understood the slogans, I took up their clarion call and passed it on. I felt we could throw off the chains which had enslaved my ancestors. We could laugh at last at the manufacture of flags, and changing allegiances. I felt free . . . yes, free! . . . like that!'

So saying, Reuben slipped his chains from his wrists, and hurled them at a tree-stump.

'What I did not perceive at that time was, of course, that freedom for us Jews was not a political act. I understood later – in the Youth movement – that our freedom meant above all a revolution in our personal lives and ideals, a self-emancipation which could be initiated only by a determined and ruthless effort. At the stage which I had then reached, this was beyond my perception: it had no power to mar my exhilaration. I felt young . . . perhaps for the first time. My youth began at the age of fourteen, because until then I had been tied by a chain to exhausted old men and to fatalistic creeds. Ever been young, Jack?'

'I certainly have – and still am, Reuben! I've had no opportunity so far of getting old', I replied: I felt that now at last I might be able to meet Reuben on my own ground.

PART TWO

THE REBEL

CHAPTER ONE

YOUTH TRIUMPHANT

I

Tʜᴇ ꜱᴇɢʀᴇɢᴀᴛɪᴏɴ ᴏꜰ healthy and normal human beings in barbed wire cages for years on end is not the least of all the idiocies of war. The Geneva Convention on the treatment of prisoners of war laid down that prisoners should be repatriated after a certain unspecified time on humanitarian grounds. No such repatriation – except for a fraction of *grands blessés* and personnel – had as yet taken place, and now in the fifth year of war it ceased to be of interest to us. It would be too grotesque to hope that humanitarian sentiments would weigh heavily with any of the belligerents in such a war as this. There was a time when we – the long-term prisoners of anything between two and four years – had hoped for repatriation, solely on the grounds that all concerned might benefit by such an exchange. Admittedly, the troops were doing some useful work for their captors; but the officers and N.C.O's were an absolute nuisance to friend and foe. Both Germany and we could do with a couple of hundred thousand men and officers, and it was difficult to see why either side should be the chief beneficiary, and thereby spoil the willingness of the other to co-operate in such a scheme.

We failed, therefore, to understand why the negotiations between the Powers concerned broke down time and again – unless both parties did not care two hoots about their prisoners, but thought them safer out of harm's way in the care of the enemy. The fact remains that we were sore on the point. There are probably none of us who do not feel that those years in prison were years of frustration. Our military careers were shattered, contacts with new developments and experiences at home were broken off, and many deep personal ties were subjected to a severe and often unbearable strain by the enforced separation.

But although nothing could compensate us for the loss of freedom, there is another side to the question: and I cannot help insisting on the fact that we prisoners had unwillingly entered upon what may perhaps prove to have been the outstanding experience of our lives. Such experience is a gain, even if it cannot be measured in pecuniary terms. The gain to which I am referring is the bringing to life of one of the formative factors in the character of man; that which moulds him into a thinking and active member of the community, as opposed to the lone wolf symptomatic of our modern civilization. I believe that the experiences of the battlefield, followed up by captivity, cut deeply into our emotional and conscientious selves. A sequence of adventures, each of which meant the facing of death, followed by military defeat and failure – what in fact the early stages of the war amounted to for the allied forces – leading up eventually to captivity with its own manifold sensations, could not fail to force on us a contemplative search of heart.

I know that many of my friends were quite scared when they found themselves assailed by thoughts, speculations, investigations, and even prickings of conscience. They quite sincerely felt it to be a somewhat 'un-British' way of reacting to something which might after all be merely ascribed to bad luck. Some even succeeded in shaking off the new attitude, and turned unconcernedly to their substitute occupations and amusements.

Others – and they formed a considerable and not altogether an inferior minority – accepted that hitherto unexperienced shock with an open-minded readiness. One cannot survive such upheavals without being confronted by unpleasant whys and wherefores. I believe myself to be a fair representative of that group. I come of good North-country stock, with the blood of Midlothian cattle-lifters also in my veins. I was always decently cared for, I knew no hardships and felt no antagonism to my elders. Traditions and class prejudices came down to me, but were mellowed by a sound streak of common sense and sceptical humanism. I had the education of a gentleman, and my life at college and in the Army consisted of the correct balance – so I believe – of work and pleasure. I had seen something of the world – Europe, India, and the Near East – and I did not just assume that everything was all right, with God in His heaven and man on his earth. I realised even before the war, that our economy and politics were in a muddle, but I had a tender spot in my heart for this good old English state of affairs, with its inevitable happy outcome. Though I knew that the world around us was getting out of joint, I was not seriously concerned about it – I knew from my bit of history that it wasn't the first time that the British people had found themselves faced with toppling worlds. I groused about the policy of our governments – Mr. Churchill's speeches and line of thought alone struck a vibrating note in my heart – but I took no great interest, always assuming that they 'probably knew what they were about'. In that frame of mind I moved down from Palestine to Marsa Matruh, when the war broke out.

But on entering the gates of my first prison camp there was little left of my pre-war indifference. A great many of my friends and fellow-prisoners found themselves facing the same challenge. New and as yet undefined experiences came upon us with the force of sledge hammers. Let me mention a few of them: death and crippling of young friends; devastation of what we called the symbols of Western civilization; hunger and starvation – of which we had scarcely heard before, and certainly never experienced; comradeship in the field of battle and in hunger, of all classes, nations and creeds – a galaxy of human solidarity, courage and cowardice, upsetting many preconceived ideas; bankrupt leadership of our superiors in the army and in politics, men previously beyond the reach of doubt or criticism; manifestations of democracy and of fascist dictatorship which concerned our personal fate as never before; the effect of selfishness or altruism of a few on the life of whole communities – an utterly abstract moral sermon before war and captivity, now become part of real individual experience. It was a vast range of human emotion and reaction, known to us before as providing the subject-matter of novels, but never putting us personally to the test. Admittedly the stress of our condition was not comparable with the normal course of things in pre- or post-war periods. War and captivity not only create new problems, they actually magnify the elements of life of a peace-time society. Everything we found in war was existent before it in the make-up of our social and political life, though camouflaged by a vast net of sham, or the blindness of habit. With the end of war, everything tends to find a new balance: what balance is it to be this time?

From literature and other sources, we learned that much of the disillusionment and stagnation in our political-economic life, as well as in morals, was due to the fact that the best of our youth had left their bones on the battlefields in the first world war. The old men, and the wreckage of the younger generation who survived, were said either to have been exhausted or to have lost themselves in the fever of indulging in compensations for missed pleasures.

To-day we were, I hoped, entitled to the belief that our casualties would be light when compared with the last war, and that the mass of our younger generation would return home safely. The question arises, what is this generation going to do, at home and in the Dominions? Are we bringing with us a programme; a faith and a willingness to serve our people, or are we again going to drown in the mire of night-clubs on the one hand, and 'distressed areas' on the other? I share in the belief that this time we shall keep our heads, and shall ask not for wild pleasures but for work and leadership. We are willing, and I believe quite capable of playing our part in the building up of the life of our peoples on the basis of our experience and of lessons learnt.

We in captivity also spoke of reconstruction and of a new England, and even of a new Commonwealth of the British nations. These terms appeared to be vague and non-committal, but it would be a great mistake to conclude that they had no meaning for us. There was probably no unanimity of programme amongst us, but there was an all-embracing unanimity of purpose for the materialization of the great humanitarian ideals. It is not surprising that our present younger generation lacks a comprehensive programme. Our political training was most superficial, and consequently we followed quite willingly – with minor rebellious exceptions – in the wake of our fathers. It was good and beneficial as long as it lasted. This war brought us suddenly, and none too gently to earth, and it was extremely surprising to find such a high degree of understanding prevailing amongst those who talked things over. We agreed as to the basic principles on which our economy, politics, education and social security should be established, though the ways to be used for their realisation were by no means decided at once.

Many of us had recovered faith in the church, and wished to see in her the instrument for the materialization of a higher social morality, by which we meant the elimination of both social extremes – want and parasitic wealth. Many more believed in the same objective, but considered a political party as the only adequate instrument for such a purpose. Others desired to see the instrument in the form of free organisations, like trade unions, co-ops, and professional groups. But there was scarcely any difference of opinion as to the actual objective of future social policy. In fact, individual party attachments did not seem to stand in the way of radical programmes advocated by one and all. Self-styled

Conservatives advocated nationalisation of land with as much fervour, and probably with more understanding, than Labour intellectuals. Schemes proposing equal opportunity of education for all, and the reform of the House of Lords, were considered just as seriously by Tories and Liberals as by Socialists and Communists.

I venture to suggest that present-day Party denominations do not cover the actual inclinations and views held by our present younger generation. It seemed rather doubtful whether we should feel ourselves comfortable within the framework of Party life at home. In fact there was an alignment of ideals among us, which strictly speaking, knew of only one demarcation line.

On one side we had the democratic group, professing adherence to a social programme based on a planned and partly nationalised economy, and on the principle of national responsibility for feeding, housing and education of all members of the community. It was understood that the greater power given to the community as a whole, should in no way eliminate the democratic institutions, and absolute individual liberty in all spheres of the spiritual life.

The other was the communist, revolutionary camp which – though working for the realisation of the same ideals – did not believe that our democratic institutions (even when reformed) would be capable or willing to carry out such a radical change in our lives, and demanded a much more forceful policy.

It would be the natural thing if the returning younger generation made an attempt to re-organise political life, not on the basis of past traditions and their divergent historical origins, but on the basis of the present unity of purpose. Why should we not agree that Socialist analysis and remedies have scored the predicted victory over the atomised material civilization? And can Socialists deny that our democracy has stood the strain and stress of time, and proved adequate to allow for the changes of our political and social set-up? Young Conservatives, Liberals and Socialists have much more in common at present than their predecessors, and it is to them that we must look for a basically united and purposeful leadership in the post-war period. It appeared to us that only the youth of the parties concerned possesses the vital unity of purpose and freedom from Party prejudices to start the nation off on its truly revolutionary task.

Here my writing and high flights of reasoning were brought

abruptly to an end by the most violent daylight raid of U.S. heavy bombers ever carried out over the Brunswick area, whither our camp had recently been moved. For the past ten minutes I had been aware of a faint buzzing of planes round the camp, then a violent A.A. barrage indicated that I had better stop and think about shelter. Indeed, I had scarcely looked out through the window, when I saw the bomber formations sailing right over the camp and a shower of silver fishes come raining down. I made straight for the basement, but before I reached it an enormous roar of express trains and clouds of dust from inside and around the camp made us all painfully aware of the position in which the Germans had put us.

Our camp – Oflag 79 – had been placed – on purpose, we understood – in the centre of alluring military objectives. To the North and North-East, joining straight on to the camp, were aerodromes. To the West and South-West were the industrial plants of the NIEMOR (Niederschlesische Motorworks), and the industrial area and city of Brunswick. In the woods about our camp had been hidden A.A. batteries and probably dumps of all descriptions. The setting up of a P.O.W. camp in such surroundings either meant that our presence provided protection to vital military installations or submitted us to the effect of our own air attacks. We had experienced any number of day and night raids on the area: and we had been surprised and happy to realise that the allied pilots knew our location, and had always managed – no mean feat, considering our position – to hit everything round us and yet spare the camp. So it had come about that we were lulled into an exuberant feeling of security. And when, on that morning of August 24th, a hail of bombs of all calibres came down on the area, including our own camp, we were caught napping. Three killed, nine seriously injured, and about thirty slightly injured was the total of our casualties. Every building had several direct hits, but nevertheless we had a miraculous escape. About ten bombs of heavy calibre missed our quarters by inches, and landed in the open spaces between the buildings. There was scarcely a window left unbroken and the camp looked a shambles: but compared with the damage done to the German quarters outside the barbed wire, and to the main objective (the factory area), the damage caused was trifling. Our people dealt so efficiently with the incendiaries, and even with unexploded anti-personnel bombs, that none of our quarters caught fire, while every building inhabited or used by the Germans was burnt down. It would be idle to deny that we were badly shaken, and it must have been evident to us that no technical device, nor any amount of care taken by our pilots, could make sure of leaving our camp unscathed.

II

Our study group proceeded happily and ambitiously. We found the part played by youth in world history a surprisingly refreshing and unexplored terrain. We observed that a nation which is incapable of meeting change by steady revolutionary modification must, almost without exception, face a crisis: and in this crisis rebellious youth comes to the fore. The great part played by youth in the revolutionary epochs of France, Russia and Germany, demonstrates clearly that our contention is well founded. It also demonstrates clearly the invigorating force which youth releases in society, and the violence resulting from the artificial blocking of the essential evolutionary law determining man's progress.

Societies which maintain a healthy metabolism – such as our own in the British Isles – feel seldom, if ever, the violent attacks of organized youth. And our own experience is borne out by other nations which develop without critical convulsions. In such cases the transition from boyhood to the spheres of activity of the adult is made smooth by a wisely-balanced system: in our own case, often making use of physical diversions. In this particular case the question arises whether too much vigour may thus be diverted, and absorb too much of the potential of youth, which might otherwise go to the vitalisation of the nation.

On the nature of youth we consulted many authorities. Almost all, to our delight, condemned certain prejudicial pronouncements of age. For some old men and women seem to believe that youth is merely immaturity, and has, as a result, no direct vital contribution to make to society. Both biology and psychology tell a different story. (We may be excused the statement, *en passant*, that we accepted the verdict of biology, as an exact science, but accorded to psychology at best the position of a branch of systematizing philosophy). They agree, and insist that a man or woman of fifty has not a speck more of brain than the youth of eighteen or twenty, but is, on the other hand, physically liable to slight decay. This does not impede his mental potential, but is a handicap where vigorous outer action may be required.

We ventured to maintain that England could have faced the crisis of peace and war better, had youth had a greater share in her leadership. When the crisis finally came – the crisis at the moment being one of war and not revolution – only then was the appeal made to youth. Even then there was much inertia, and many of our young leaders were obstructed. The exploits of Wingate and Stirling, amongst others, show how they learnt to hit back and to overcome this obstruction. It is encouraging to note that they got the support of the best of the older generation. In this case we may take it that the crisis gave an outlet to the vigour of youth.

Is it too much to assume that the tasks of peace will be any less demanding than the tasks of war? Rather it seems as if the many political ideals coming to fruition in the present war will call for a possibly greater endeavour and effort on the part of youth. Political and social programmes need not be right in our eyes because they were right a century ago, but only insofar as they help toward a scientific solution of current problems. Our fathers indeed were too wise and adventurous to accept without modification that which was handed down to them.

We know that we, and only we, are capable of such an objective and unobstructed approach to these problems, and we are determined to fulfil our obligation. The birthright of youth should this time not be sold for a game of cricket or a cocktail!

III

The discussions and arguments we in our circle had on this topic – composed as it was of potential M.P's, clergymen, school-masters, party functionaries, social workers, insurance agents ('Oh, and what about the Beveridge Plan?'), and other related busybodies – provided the opportunity not only of airing our own views, but also – and this was, after all, my chief concern, in view of this book – of getting on with Reuben's story.

The experience of his own generation had led him to acquire an unbounded belief in youth, which became at times an obsession with him. He admitted frankly that youth can be made an agent of chauvinism or nihilism when exploited by unscrupulous dema-gogues, as fascism and nazism have proved. But he pointed out to me that destructiveness is not a peculiarity of youth alone; on the other hand, enthusiasm, drive, honesty, pioneering spirit, and a minimum of prejudices are youth's innate attributes. If these are permitted to lie fallow, a nation is robbed of its most valuable asset. Nevertheless, Reuben thought it his duty to warn me against publishing the story of his own youth – his seven fat years – for reasons which will become apparent from his own words. I decided not to heed this warning, but to give his story as he told it. After all, what is the good of being young if you do not dare to fling defiance in the face of the world?

'Well, Mr. Jack Inquisitor', Reuben addressed me in response to my expostulations, 'I shall do as you bid: but I must warn you that every word I say will serve as evidence against you on the day of judgment. Please remember that on that glorious day – which, if the precision bombing of our camp continues, may not be far off – I shall have a privileged approach to the Judge, and then where will you be? I know – don't get contradictory, you are taking notes in order to commercialise my private affairs. But instead of counting your guineas, you will most probably count your bruises. Please consider that my compatriots – the Jews of the older generation, and those parading Piccadilly and Broadway – will boycott you and your book, for giving vent to the story of a godless, heretical fellow, a rebel against his own father (may he rest in peace!). Your own people won't touch it either – haven't they had enough of Jewboys? What interest or moral can they find in the rebellious life of a scion of the most bigoted race on God's earth? In short, dear Jack, you sow the wind and will rightly reap the whirlwind. I am not afraid for my own reputation, if I have one: but you, Jack . . . With so many prizes in wait for you, associating yourself with . . . All right, all right, don't get cross, you shall have your pound of flesh – not bloodless, though.

'Do you remember my asking you the other day whether you had ever been young? You replied haughtily to my apparently stupid question. Will it surprise you then to hear that my people have never been young, and that my own and preceding generations had to dig themselves out from the ashes of grey-bearded scholasticism, and from the wreckage of physical senility? We should probably have failed to do it, were it not for the powerful gusts of fresh air blowing down on us from over the Carpathians and Dniester.

'Remember, the war was over, and the abyss into which European civilization was destined to fall was still hidden, by the mists of joy, from the survivors of a cataclysm of unprecedented fury. Fifteen millions killed and maimed, and as many millions dead of famine and influenza – who can blame the young in their hunt for anæsthetics to drown their fears and despair? You in England and in the other victorious nations were groping for compensation for lost love and pleasure. In our region youth found compensation in revolution and nationalistic chauvinism. The three great empires of East and Centre – Russia, Austria, Germany – the symbols of national and social oppression, lay in splinters at our feet; and we believed that the dawn of a new era had broken. The young peoples of Eastern Europe were now masters in their own house and became to their undoing harsh masters in other people's houses as well. The proletariat of Central and Western Europe, led by its intellectuals, was grasping for the moon. With the tyrants gone, and social and national oppression at an end, could there be any obstacle in the way of realisation of the millennium? Chaos, civil-war, hunger, brigandage? Admittedly inconveniences, but who would be discouraged by such trifles? Is not chaos the primordial material out of which order and beauty are shaped? (Thermodynamic laws had by then not yet crossed the Carpathians: I wonder whether they have since?). Moreover, when you are young you scorn the questions of the sober, sceptical realist.

'It was the heydey of youth: dreamers, revolutionaries, reformers . . . and charlatans too. "A new world it is going to be, and woe to him who dares to block the way. We are young and youth is beautiful ran the hymn of the German youth movement. Out of the rotten timber of the old world a new shining Jerusalem will arise. Are you a sceptic? Don't you believe it? Do you shake your white locks? They might have pitied you, O ye of little faith! But pity was an alien product of yesterday: it reeked of mould and hypocrisy. So they will destroy you, unless you stop clicking your tongue.

' "We shall march over corpses and graves, we shall climb the highest peaks, communing with sun and blizzard, and nothing in between!

' "We shall . . . We shall . . . We shall . . .", they cried, and kicked the wiseacres out of their path. And from over the Dniester came the roar of guns and of consuming flames, under which the old régime was being stamped out."

'Sparks from those mighty fires fell on the dry shavings of our own youth, and kindled them to a blaze. Should we join our flames to the fire of all the young? Should we storm bastilles others had built? Should we assist the revolution of the proletariat, in which we had no part? Should we rejoice over the substitution of Ferdinand I, the King of All the Rumanians, for Francis Joseph or Carol? It made no appeal to many of my generation. What about turning our looks inwards to our own homes? Were there no bastilles to be stormed, thrones to be torn down? Were there no smothered souls to be liberated? Should we stand idly by when the whole world was spring-cleaning, and blowing gargoyle idols to hell?

'We, the Jewish youth – or as many as had the stomach for it – took up the torch. We soaked it in the highly inflammable substance of the new romance, woven by our Halutzim (Pioneer settlers) on the Lake of Galilee: and we lit it from the blaze enveloping us from West and East. The ancient bastion of Galut (Diaspora) caught fire; many outworks were cleared up; the core of it became undermined; but we were still waiting for the finale.

'You are getting tired of my endless symbolism? I sympathise: but, to be honest, I must speak in the language and pictures of my youth. The symbols were the realities for us, to the exclusion of everything else. We continued, of course, to do our chores. We went to school, did our lessons, kept up appearances to some extent. But that was the sum total of concessions made by us to the routine of home-life, and the community of our elders. Our life did not focus round home and school. Our home was in our own clubs, in attics, or suburban shacks. Camps, and around the camp fires, in forest and meadow, these were our peripatetic academies. The peaks and gorges of the Carpathians were our synagogue, the stars and moon its dome. New, hitherto unknown sensations took hold of us. I still feel the sensation – alarm, turning into joyous thrill – when we discovered our bodies.

'Yes, the body, Jack! We did not know there was such a thing. No, I am not fooling you: what was the body to us? A sinful, evil earthly shell to house our immortal souls. What should be done to it? Hide it, cloak it, torture it. And when you must give it its unspeakable due – but hush! – don't utter a word about it. Our scholarly teachers sighed in surprise at the Creator having put our soul – which may commune with archangels and patriarchs in the crystal paradise – into such a profane, vulgar, animal container.

' "Keep down the lust of your flesh: if you must give way to it on the sly, then blush for the frolicking of your blood, and for the ripple of your muscles."

'Such was the lesson dinned into our ears for generations on end. Hellenic heathendom, expressed in the cult of shameless nakedness, was it not smitten by the Macabees for ever and ever? Our fathers and mothers felt no desire to correct the verdict of the Macabees. Wait, Jack, I shall soon wipe out your superior grin. It was the same lesson given to you Gentiles by Christianity. You displayed more sense, because your ancestors came from the forest and not from the desert, but you scarcely shared the more uncompromising honesty of my ancestors. The Judaic attitude to the body was taken up by Christianity in its entirety: but whereas my people were encouraged to adhere to that strange misinterpretation by circumstances, and probably by a lack of sense of worldly proportion peculiar to my race, you gentiles of the Western world enjoyed a comfortable compromise between the good of this world, demonstrated by earthly Hellenism, and the kingdom of the soul in the other, ethereal, world. In principle we stand on the same platform, although parsons play cricket and Rabbis don't – oh, yes, they do now in your part of the world . . .

'At the stage with which I am dealing, the sensation of the discovery of the body was overshadowing every theory, creed or prejudice. The sickening paleness of our skins was exposed adoringly to sun and wind: the flabby, stooping stature became the playground of rippling muscle. We could not have enough of sun and air. Long trousers, collar and tie, tightly buttoned coats – once the dream of the young, and insignia of adulthood – were eschewed, even as the pig was eschewed by our elders. Shorts, open-neck shirts, sandals, and short-cropped hair, flourished in their stead. Then sun and wind, rain and snow came to heal our wounds. They could in a like fashion heal and enliven our girls, hitherto fettered by styles either orthodox or "voguish". Both styles went by the board – the "chastity" dress and pigtail, under which girlish freshness was smothered, and the other extreme of obscenely exaggerated bust and buttock, and savagely disfigured lip and eyebrow. Shorts and blazer in camp, and neat simple skirt or linen gown, with hair fluttering in the breeze – then did our girls become proud, strong and independent human beings, whom we could love, and whom believe me, we only then learnt to respect.

'I don't mind, Jack, if you remark about the banality of my

enthusiasm in matters so trivial and commonplace to-day. But remember, all this happened five and twenty years ago, and took place in countries where men used padding for their jackets, and where officers of the army wore corsets, and indulged in lipstick and powder. And in those countries my contemporaries wore the kaftan and grew beards and sidelocks, or paraded gigolo-fashion on the boulevards, and kept their appointments in the brothels. Our dress was not a uniform with us, as with the boy scouts, but an expression of our negation of the society and its moral standards in which we found ourselves. Our cultivation of the body, which never deteriorated into a cult on its own, or into pugilistic athletics for that matter, was only the first visible step towards the adoption of a new discipline of life.

'Before I joined the youth movement they had difficulty in getting me up from bed in time for school: afterwards I was up at six for morning runs or sunrise meetings with my group. It was perplexing for my family, because they felt intuitively that my new style spoke of too much free-will, and independence of home training. When I came to rub down my body with freshly fallen snow, and refused to touch alcohol in any form, I was at last given up as stark mad: this suited my purpose very well, because they ceased to pamper me. Week-ends and vacations saw me packing my rucksack to set out hiking in the country – no matter whether permission was granted or withheld. It was usually withheld: for was I not a delicate child, scarcely out of my rickets and measles: was I not pale, skinny and without appetite? They gaped though, when I returned from camp; tanned, frolicking and full of life. As to appetite, well I have never gone back, as you know! We had no intention of sneaking out of town to avoid the jeering crowds who spat at us to abjure Satan, when we boys and girls marched by, led by mandolines and mouthorgans, shouting defiance at the young-old dandies. The Rabbis in the synagogues harangued the people against the young bareheaded heretics, marching off into camp with their unchaperoned girls. Disgusting libels were set afoot by the men of God and the brothel-youth about our morals. How could those with their snouts in the dung-heap grasp what purifying power lay in morning dews and sunsets watched from majestic peaks? How could they be expected to understand the pride we took in our virginity and the notion we had of love, which was for us the privilege of physically and intellectually mature men and women.

Their town love we called prostitution – dowry, matrimonial agency, agreements between parents on the sale of their daughters, economic serfdom for women. And we made no bones about it. Our elders and compatriots reared on tradition, could not sit down under our challenge. They knew we were out to tear up their world root and branch.

' "Was that all?" you ask. No. I have dealt so far with mere externals. There were much deeper issues between the two generations who were facing one another across the barriers. They now trained their heavy guns on us.

'We had ceased to be Jews, they proclaimed, and threatened to excommunicate us. Well, if Judaism meant beards and corkscrew curls, the hubbub of the synagogue, and the rumbling of prayers whose content was known but to few, they were certainly right. Did Judaism mean, not striking a match on the Sabbath; eating kosher and not speaking Hebrew; praying for a return to Jerusalem and never going there; believing in a God of revengeful wrath and slaughtered lambs while being addicted to money-lending, shopkeeping and business? It meant all this for many of those across the barrier. For us, this was all synonymous with human degradation and patriarchal superstition. We said so.

' "You are a godless lot with no religion", they thundered at us from their pulpits, and across the counters of their banks and shops. We were on distinctly dangerous ground. Did they mean the God personified by our nomadic ancestors 3,000 years ago, or God the accomplished mechanic, or God the snooper with the swords of revenge? We felt sincerely, and sometimes desperately, that such a god was not and could not be our god. In that sense we were, of course, godless. And religion? A volume of pre-scribed prayers and an uncritical collection of sublime poetry and obscure mumble-jumble – religion? A string of ritual performances, probably gracious enough for Babylonians and Egyptians or for mediæval Rabbis – no, we distinctly and frankly had nothing in common with that religion.'

At this point of his narrative I thought it was wise to interrupt the flow of Reuben's memories. I could see him clearly as a youth. Ruthless in his negation, and fanatical as his race made him. He was now approaching his fortieth birthday: I knew that he had won through to a more kindly attitude towards life and men, and I wanted to find out whether his positive and rather humorously sceptical views of to-day had already been there in his youth.

Reuben had told me again and again that those traditions he had so hotly fought against had preserved the Jewish race, and many of its qualities which have made valuable intellectual contributions to our civilization. I reminded him of his many apologies, and the kindly patience he had so often shown, to the aberrations of men and peoples. I said as much to him, in an effort to bring him round to a more positive line. He listened to my remonstrances with bowed head, and when he took up his story again he opened mildly enough, but he soon threw his protest at me: 'Goodness me, Jack, do you want me to come down to cowardly extenuations and apologies for the sins of my youth in order to make your book respectable? I wish every youth lived such a life as I have, and I wish nothing better for my son. Should he find my way of life incompatible with his own notions, then I expect him to go his own way, and he shall have my blessing. And if you conclude from what I have told you so far, that our main object was to scatter the layers of débris and rubbish piled up throughout the ages by the unfortunate history of my people, then you are wrong. We felt no need to define our exact position in the way of codes or principles; and were as yet unprepared to draw demarcation lines between our own generation, the past, and the future. But the society in which we found ourselves forced us, by violent and malignant attacks, to define our aims before we were actually ready for such a step.

'We had to answer the question of our relation to Judaism. We certainly felt the same attachment to our people as would any other youth: and the depth of the degradation in which we thought our people were living made us the more determined to cling to the bright patches of our history. The more we turned our back on the priestly and rabbinical tradition, the brighter rose for us the light of the prophets. In Isaiah and Amos we believed we had found the true core of Judaism, and the longed-for renaissance of our nation could and would come about if the revolutionary and uncompromising vigour of the prophets was accepted as the historical starting-point. Rituals, ceremonies and practices of modern medicine-men were to us crusted shells, to be discarded and crushed before a Jewish nation could live again. We could not and did not accept the passive exilic fatalism of our elders. It was easy for us to know that we were not Polish, Ukrainain, Austrian, Russian or Rumanian nationals. We saw with our sharp youthful eyes that assimilation to our neighbours was a farce which would eventually turn into tragedy. A Jewish Pole, a Jewish Rumanian, and so forth – who could respect himself under such guises? And who could expect that such tragic or despicable play-acting should be respected by others? Jewish religion was obviously for us a matter of individual choice or belief: but Jewish blood, and membership of a definite historical group – a nation – were objective realities. If the prophets became the spiritual link with our past, then Palestine, land and toil and spoken Hebrew, became the positive answer to the mere negation of the exilic and messianic submission to fate. The stand we took to face the challenge of rabbinical Judaism in no way lessened our antagonism to those of the younger Jewish generation who – lacking even the sincere if gloomy creed of our fathers – were complacently continuing to parade their Pharisaism, and flaunt their self-imposed shame, with consequences too terrible to relate.

'I remember our struggle to find an answer to the religious question (I don't mean an answer to the type of question those across the barrier were wont to ask). There was something in our life which scorned definition – yet was it not akin to religion? What made us run to meet the stormy rains, groping ecstatically for the moon, while our leader read to us passages from Tagore, Zarathustra or Gœthe? Was it adolescent romanticism, or something deeper and more lasting? We also used to celebrate the Sabbath in the camp in our own way. On Saturday eve we were to be found in a clearing of the woods; blazing torches would light the circular piece of ground, with a trench cut round it, which served as a table. Then from the forest came the stirring vibrations of a violin, playing Beethoven, Mozart or Chopin: and this was followed by a pianissimo communal song to welcome the day of rest for all toiling men. Finally, before getting down to our sandwiches – on which longing looks were concentrated – somebody said grace. He or she said anything they liked. I remember the grace I spoke once – want to hear it?

' "Brothers and sisters", I said, "Let us give thanks to the men and women who toiled to produce our bread. Let us love the beauty and purposefulness of nature, which gives fruit to the toil and love of man. Let us help our unfortunate people, and bring it back through us to Eretz Israel, to be again tillers of the soil and workers in stone. Let us go as a community, united to help each other, in days of stress and of joy."

'Was that a religious ritual? We should have been shocked if

74

someone had suggested it: but it was and gave colour to our life, and added to our emotions, and much of it remains with us to this day.

'No book had for us the stamp of holiness: Bible, Gospel, Veda, Spinoza, mystics, poets – we felt the same about them, as long as they appealed to our sincere longings to be clean and honest, and fortified us in our belief that man is far better than he seems to realise. We contemplated with the mystic, speculated with the free-thinker, sang with the poet, marvelled with the naturalist, dreamed with the Utopians and walked with the seers. Give it any name you like, jeer at it over your sophisticated cocktails – but one who has not lived it might as well never have been born. Yes, of course, we felt olympic and superior and looked down on those worms crawling in the slime of boulevards and gutters. We were not exclusive: on the contrary, we went out to boulevard, gutter, and mansion too, to pick them up one by one, boys and girls. The sons and daughters of the rich, and of the beggars at the cemetery gate found themselves in our midst, in the same group living the same life.

'Nevertheless, we knew ourselves to be an aristocracy, and we were elated, and had unbounded confidence in our way of life. It was so, not only because of the speed at which we moved, but also through the quality and amount of instruction we packed into the few hours of our daily meetings. Philosophy, natural sciences, the arts, music, Hebrew, history, geography and related subjects concerning Palestine and the old Mediterranean civilizations – all of it slightly haphazard and raw, but how fresh! We put every penny we could lay our hands on into our library and arts fund. We were probably the first in that region to introduce Freud, Adler and Jung, as well as Gustav Landauer, H. G. Wells and other progressive thinkers, to the public. We were encouraged to try our hand at verse and prose, to be read out at the evening meetings in our shacks, with discussions to follow. It was a glorious life for us young Jews. And I may state it without undue vanity – one cannot live entirely without it, you know! – that this experience of our youth gave us health, and yet preserved us from brutishness; it made us proud and yet humble, idealists and yet no mere windmill knights. It was sweet as long as it lasted. And fortunately for us, our objective conditions forced us through that danger that lurks for all youth movements, the danger of running to seed. We were never to resemble those grown-ups who remain, all their lives, boy scouts fumbling with knots, or that other type of white-haired man who never ceases to be stupidly puerile.

'The conditions of our life necessitated an early decision – far too early for our liking. The day came all too soon when the die was cast, and we had to leave home to go out into the desert. It was the first crisis of our community, and many fine friends and leaders of ours succumbed. It was that crisis that shot me up to the leadership of our community – fortunately preceded by a steady and stringent process of training."

I let the matter rest at that.

In his reminiscences, Reuben mentioned many lively scenes. One was his initiation as a sworn member of the movement: this took place at a camp in the mountains, in an hour of thrilling thunder and lightning. Moses must have been a great dramatic producer in his day, and a good psychologist, Reuben remarked, concerning the setting for his initiation. Then there was the incident of the Rabbi who warned him not to go bare-headed, for a stone from Heaven might strike him down: to whom he retorted that in that case he would hide behind a Gentile, since the latter appeared to be immune against stones from Heaven. And then there was a time when Reuben and his companions found their club-shack raided and obscenely defiled by a group of orthodox fanatics; they duly employed a stratagem, ambushed the suspected gang, and meted out retribution. There were many more of these colourful episodes which I omit, as being irrelevant to the main theme.

If all goes well with us here in Brunswick I shall yet have the continuation of the story: for Reuben is very keen to get it off his chest before our idle routine is ended by collapse, chaos, and final liberation.

CHAPTER TWO

HAGSHAMAH

I

I ALWAYS EXPERIENCED GREAT difficulty in obtaining descriptions of people and places from Reuben. His contention was always that people would not be interested in extraneous details, their sole desire would be to follow the development of the story.

However, I believe the reader will agree with me that characterisation and topographical descriptions do play a great part in helping us to re-create a story in our own minds. I carried my point with Reuben, and shall now continue my task considerably lightened by his promises of co-operation.

These boys and girls and their leaders, few of them over twenty years of age, were reaching the point in their lives when the bracing effects of personal fulfilment and self-realisation would no longer be adequate for their ideas. The glorious intrinsic romance of being young, and knowing it, is good while it lasts: but eventually the time had to come when they would feel a longing for action and service. In fact, they believed that it was not only imperative, but actually possible, to find a mould of adult life in which their idealism could be cast, and take practical political shape. Some of them had finished school, and the routine termini – university, academy, workship, bank, and commerce – were ready to receive a cargo of new victims. If they were to submit to it, they argued, their idealism would be ground to dust: and of all their dreams and heart-aches, only a nostalgic memory would survive. Many groups of youngsters – though as yet few in proportion – had an answer ready to hand. These, Reuben among them, left school, banks, commerce and home itself, and all the prizes held out to them by their upbringing, and hired themselves out as farmhands or industrial workers. They did this in order to develop their bodies and minds for collective life in Palestine, a life based on manual labour. Such a move could not fail to arouse both ridicule and anger amongst their parents: but it also challenged the whole adolescent body of the youth movement to follow their example, or to find an alternative compatible with their ideals.

The movement I am referring to, which was called 'The Young Watchers', numbered about 2,000 boys and girls. It had by that time adopted a definite organisational and educational scheme. The 10-13 year olds – called the 'Audients' or those who listen (all names and terms were in Hebrew) – followed under their leaders a scheme intended to sharpen their senses, and to arouse their curiosity in the workings of nature outside their own egos; the 13-16 year olds, called the 'Scouts', followed a scheme based on the scouting technique, which also embraced more intellectual fields as well as the romance of camp life. The 16 year olds and over, called the 'Workers' (whose work was carried on in study-groups, seminaries, vacational hiking tours, and eventually in groups organised for agricultural training) assumed the leadership of the juniors, and were the finished product of the movement. Any decision taken by the Workers was bound to have its repercussions on the education of all those in the junior age-groups.

The problem of which way of life the Workers would choose was argued throughout the movement for a year, and a feeling of impending crisis hung overhead. The annual convention of the leaders and Workers was given the task of clearing the air, and answering the question: how best could idealism be carried into the life of an adult Jew?

As the conventions of the movement were never held in town, the Executive chose for the present assembly a spot in the Bistriza valley. The Bistriza, digging its way through the South-East Carpathians, forms one of the most picturesque valleys in that mountain range; seen from the Alpine pastures sloping down from the forest belt, the golden Bistriza has inspired some of the best lyrics of the Rumanian and Hungarian poets. In one of these meadows, within easy reach of the river, the convention established itself in a collection of hay-barns and sheds, in which the peasants used to store their hay crop for the winter, in order to feed the cattle that come down from the alps.

It was a hot, lazy, August day, when batches of boys and girls with mountain-high packs on their backs came climbing up the ascent to their quarters. Some of them came from the junior camps – which had closed down after a month's activity – and others straight from their homes all over the country. With them came also delegations from kindred Jewish movements throughout Eastern Europe. The delegation from Poland emphasised in its turn-out its strongly scouting characteristics; the Viennese and Czechoslovakian parties in leather shorts, heavy mountain boots, and with the inevitable guitar, represented more the type of free unregimented youth: while the small, rather miserable-looking group of the Hungarian Jewish youth wore a partly bourgeois and partly tramp outfit which betrayed them as being mere green-horns in the youth movement.

There was also Reuben's group to a man – eight boys and two girls – who had been on the march for two days. It wouldn't do to arrive by train or 'bus like trippers travelling to Marienbad. Their faces, burnt and dusty, mirrored the exhilaration which comes from an open-air life. They sang as they marched, and their teasing and jokes at the expense of the stragglers hobbling on their blistered heels and tender feet were echoed back by the mountains.

On arrival inside the stockade of the camp, they found quarter-masters there to welcome them, and show them to their quarters – barn floors, and attics piled high with scented hay. The overseer of the girls' quarters, Naomi, a comfortable broad-beamed girl with gigantic spectacles on her stumpy nose, bustled her charges about, while shrieks of greeting and exchanges of experiences of camp life and hiking were hurled across from group to group. 'Look at Judith's nose!' It was swollen to a 'hundred' times its normal size after a few hornets had made contact with it. 'And Naomi, I must have a swim in the lovely river and a change of my knickers, because I am awfully sweaty!'

The cook, a butcher's apprentice by the look of him, and his flock of assistants, had a gigantic maize mash bubbling on the camp cookers: and he would like to know how many hungry mouths were actually expected, since the secretariat had failed to hand in the required returns. By the look of his stores, he would probably be bankrupt in no time, unless Tsvi, the greatest diplomat the movement ever produced, could manage to wheedle more money out of the pockets of those who hated the movement and yet contributed to its funds.

The evening of the same day saw the opening of the convention. About three hundred Workers and their guests, all dressed in their best camp outfits, assembled in the barn, now transformed into a conference hall: there was a dais for the Executive, a Speaker's stand, and rough benches for the delegates. The opening ceremony was short. The hymn of the movement, 'Strengthen the hand of those who tend our land', and a violin recital with a few bars of Beethoven's 'Eroica', marked the opening. Levy, the founder and senior of the movement, delivered his opening address.

Levy was twenty-two years old, and a medical student. At the age of sixteen he had laid the foundations of the movement, and had remained at the helm ever since. In his sandals, shorts, and snow-white polo shirt, with his tousled chestnut hair, he looked the symbol of coolness and sanity. His complexion was of a yellowish leathery tint, and his slightly slanted eyes sparkled and shone as he laughed and greeted old and new friends. He was the grandson of a highly-revered Rabbi, and inherited his lucid outlook on men and life. There was no one to match him in mountaineering and the search for Edelweiss: but his passion was astronomy, and his tales of Einstein, the expanding universe, and Hershel, enlivened many an evening round the camp fire.

Levy had little to say that evening. 'Far be it from me,' he opened in his even bell-like voice, 'to interfere with, or anticipate the views to be exchanged tomorrow'. He asked the speakers and audience to be fair, and understanding of their friends' views. The fact that they appeared to differ was not the fault or virtue of any individual, but the result of the intricate state in which the Jewish people and the whole world found themselves. 'We are groping in the dark,' he added, 'and there is only one unfailing guide to consult. That is the uncompromising honesty of our own conscience.' He finished his address with the story of a Rabbi who had in front of him two fiercely-contesting parties. After the first litigant had finished his case, the Rabbi said: 'Yes, it appears to me you are right'. When the opposing party had made his statement, the Rabbi summed up once more with the remark that he was right. Such a pronouncement was exasperating to the Rabbi's secretary, who exclaimed: 'Oh, Rabbi, how can both parties be right?' To that the Rabbi answered pontifically: 'You, my boy, are also right'. There was nothing for the litigants to do but to settle their dispute by a free agreement. With that Levy handed over the stage to the artists.

In a series of living tableaux, accompanied by verse and music, the main epochs of Jewish history were shown, starting in the desert and finishing up in a settlement on the Jordan. Songs and folk-dances went on till midnight, when a bugle-call sent all to their quarters. In the silence of the night, two night-watchmen, relieved every two hours, made their rounds of the camp, whistling to the tune of the last ecstatic dance, 'Oh, Erez Israel, how have I forsaken thee . . . .'

II

After an early morning run, the whole chattering crowd was to be seen splashing in the river till the bugle announced breakfast. Mugs of cocoa and huge slabs of buttered bread were hastily consumed as all were eager for the opening of the convention. Reuben entered the barn and took his seat on the front bench. He saw the dais, from which the Executive would conduct the proceedings, strewn with evergreen, and the tables bearing peasant pottery bowls of freshly-plucked flowers. The crowd was surging in, equipped with note-books and pencils. A few artistic boys and girls, carrying cameras and sketch-books, climbed the rafters for a good bird's eye view. One by one the members of the Executive filed in. Reuben noticed the hush that always falls over an assembly when the leaders take their seats on the platform. They were older than the delegates to the convention. Reuben wondered how many of them would still be on the platform at the next convention, and who would take the empty places. He could imagine himself seated there, where the demigods dwell.

Now comes Levy, the unelected chairman of all such gatherings, whom we have seen and heard at the opening of the convention. After him Leah, the granny of the movement; twenty-four summers rest comfortably on her buxom figure. A dark blue pleated skirt, and a white jumper edged with cornflower blue, set off her pearly complexion. Her broad chubby face is framed in brown hair, cut short. She cannot help laughing and smiling benignly as she greets her boys and girls, 'so grown up' since last year. Entirely on her own, and against strong opposition, Leah founded a kindergarten, which has now grown into a chain of establishments all over the country. She has no use for note-book and pencil: instead, she will be seen knitting jumpers and socks for her little ones in the kindergarten. She insists on mixing the children of the rich and of the poor together, and makes the rich Jewesses pay for the privilege of having their children educated with those of the poor. On the left hand of Levy, a red-haired colussus plunges on to his feeble stool, which is heard to give cracking noises in protest. This fiery red giant, in his peasant shirt, split open down to his navel, nondescript shorts, and shaggy sandals on his seven-league feet, is known to all as the Torch. On his herculean neck sits a horsy face, with a pair of jaws which will crack the toughest nuts, just as his forthright tongue cracks every atom of cant and self-conceit. Torch is a born youth leader, and is at his best when he has half a dozen impish scouts climbing all over him. He is a teacher who founded his own school for deficient children – the first in the whole kingdom: and as to Freud, Jung, Adler, Pestalozzi and Froebel, there is nothing one can teach him. He rose from the poorest conditions, and for as long as he can remember he has been earning money, and looking after brothers and sisters, some older than himself. Torch is the terror of just one type in the movement – the lovesick youngsters. One girl is said to have approached him one day with her heartache, hoping to find sympathy. She got a bit of a shock when Torch said to her in his rasping voice: 'Young woman, stop making eyes at my boys, and try to become a girl again! Now listen to me. You look pale and a bit flabby. I bet you sleep on a soft bed and waste your time chewing over sickening novels. Take my advice, ducky: chuck off the double eiderdown mamma puts on your bed, take a run in the morning, and P.T. in the afternoon, a couple of showers and a swim a day. Work hard at school – I think you are not quite up to standard. Do you like growing flowers? Good, then come in the afternoons to the garden of my school and the orphanage next door. There are some lovely flowers there. All right? Yes, I love you, and all my boys will run after you as soon as you stop running after them and get down to some hard work.' It was distinctly tough on the boy or girl who was classed by Torch as a 'softie'.

Reuben viewed them all in turn as he sat there watching the crowd. It was fine to be one of them, and yet he felt something was missing. He knew precisely what it was. He had made up his mind to talk to them, and to tell them what he had found out during the last six months since he had been working as a farm-hand, carting manure, feeding oxen, ploughing good black soil. Reuben felt it in his aching bones and horny hands, quite unused now to holding a pencil. A pencil was so tiny and flimsy compared with a pitchfork. His friends in all the working communities undergoing agricultural training had charged him to tell the convention all about it.

Reuben's reflections came to an end when Levy announced that 'Grey Matter' would open the debate with an address. Baruch was nicknamed 'Grey Matter', for they believed that even the toes of his feet were made of that precious material. The son of a famous wonder-Rabbi, worshipped by thousands of Jews between Vienna and Odessa, Baruch had spent his early life among Talmudists and rabbinical candidates. His mind was sharpened like the edge of a steel blade. His physique had – perversely one would think – prospered on books. Grey Matter was stocky, broad-shouldered, with a slightly mongolian face, thick lips stretching almost from ear to ear, and a gigantic brow. His hair, had it only been allowed to grow, would have been dark. A prodigy for his age – nineteen years all told – aloof, mystical, and not to be trifled with.

Grey Matter, with an even lisping voice, spoke in finely polished sentences as if ready-shaped for the printer's ink . . .

'Brothers and sister,' Reuben was all attention, 'I have been entrusted with the task of opening the debate. I am not speaking for the Executive, nor for anybody but myself. Every delegate has the duty and the privilege of addressing the Convention and stating where he stands. Beware of following authority in your thought and talk. No personal attachments should count with you. It is good to follow a leader when you are capable of thinking for yourselves. It is complete corruption if it is the other way round. It does not matter what way you may all choose to go – those who remain faithful to the core of our movement shall meet again on that plane, on which the incorruptibles of all ages have their rendezvous: the plane of the intellect. There is no "going together" for Man, unless he is degraded to the level of herded beasts. For Man must walk his earthly way alone and lonely, rejoice at the occasional meetings with his friends, and yet never mourn the inevitable parting that will follow. From the herd rose the single man, from the movement of the young must rise the free personality. Our conference will serve to bring to light what we have gained from that movement. Are we now, after having thrown conventional lies to the wind, to surrender to a new set of racial or political conventions? According to arbitrary convention there are Jews, Rumanians, Russians and so on in the world. There is no foundation for such a sub-division of Man. There is nothing to make me the one or the other, except for a scrap of paper issued by an office. It is a mere geographical and historical

accident in the birth of a man. I may be the one or the other,
should I choose it. But should I not, the whole illusion vanishes
for me into the foul air whence it came. I am Man, that is the
only certainty of which I am aware. My blood is a composition as
unknown in its mixture to me as to those who presume to load
it with meaningless symbols – Slav, Semitic, Aryan. I was born
here in this country, but am I to be bound like a tree to the spot
where wind and gale planted my seed? I can move when and
where and in what fashion I wish. You say the world takes no
notice of my will. It is irrelevant to me whether the world be
willing to accept me or not. It is immaterial to me whether those
who call themselves civilized should persecute or slay me. I am
no more exposed to the elements of savagery than those who take
a scrap of paper as their protection. I am Man, as unique in my
personality as this earth, which has not its equal among all the
million worlds wandering in space. You say I am not realistic – a
sort of lovable but foolish Don Quixote. I am hurt and offended
for your sake when your realities are filth, superstition, chauvinism, and when "Free Man" is for you a mere metaphysical
infatuation. These so-called realities have as much relation to me
as the world of tigers and vipers. I shall not cease to be what I am
because such things are round me. You ask what I intend to do?
I intend to study, to think, and to teach. Wherever I shall find
masters and pupils for my teaching, there shall I settle. You ask
what you shall do? He who has a will and a faith will not ask
you or me what to do; and he who has it not, will join the herd
and hunt with it. The wish of many of our friends to go to Palestine and live there doing manual work within collective communities, is as good a way of life as mine. I refuse to concede
priority or superiority to any way Man chooses to go. A movement
of youth must not teach one *what* to do. All it can, and must do,
is to teach one *how* to do it. We have done that to the best of our
ability by teaching you to remain incorruptible in the face of
degradation. If we remain uncorrupted, we must often part, but
always to meet again."

On the same even tone in which he had begun, Grey Matter
finished. Reuben found himself open-mouthed, as was every boy
and girl from the ground to the rafters. It was long before the
crowd relaxed, and whispers indicated that the hypnosis of
Baruch's address, delivered in strong Biblical Hebrew, was
wearing off. Levy looked challengingly round for the next

speaker, but nobody came forward.

'Levy,' a strong girlish voice rang out over the curious crowd, 'I want to speak!'

'With pleasure, my dear Chick', replied Levy paternally.

Reuben looked round, and saw a whirl of skirts and pigtails climbing helter-skelter over bodies, to land eventually on the speakers' dais. Reuben felt his heart beating a tattoo to Chick's own fast breathing after her rush to the platform.

I was glad to have found a human spark in Reuben: indeed, he could not help blushing as he talked to me of the girl – a matter of twenty years later. Chick, according to Reuben's probably most biassed account, if not the beauty of the movement, had a captivating mischievous charm. She was of the dark Spanish type like Shakespeare's Jessica. Tall but not thin, her body was well shaped for her seventeen years, although the movement of her limbs was as yet clumsily asymmetrical, like those of a new-born lamb. Her long-shaped face sat on a good neck, and her dark brown eyes looked at the world with a merry slant. Her moist lips were half open, and their expression was a curious mixture of trembling shyness while yet impish and mischievous. Chick was known to stand in awe of nobody, which explained her daring to climb the platform after Baruch. There was another reason for it. Her family was emigrating to Palestine – one of the very few well-off families to do so in those days – and she was probably anxious to say farewell to her friends.

She spoke German with a strong Russian accent, as her parents both came from Russia.

'I enjoyed Baruch's address very much indeed', she opened with a plunge, 'but I confess there was much in it I could not understand. It happens to me often like that. When I look at a fine picture or listen to a great work of music, I feel its beauty, but I cannot get the meaning of it. I gather it does not matter in the case of art, but it is different with the words of one of us. I cannot argue with Baruch, but how many of his kind are there amongst us? He is strong enough to march alone and as he likes, but I should probably have ended among a silly crowd of cocktailers and jazzing foxtrotters if left alone. I cannot be left to work out my own destiny; I need people around me, and with the help of friends I might also be useful. So with most of us: and for such the movement is vital to their youth, and the collective life when they are old enough to do something for our people. I like Grey

Matter immensely, I have a terrible respect for him: but he wants to go alone, and we want and must go together. Thanks to my family I am off shortly to Palestine, but I imagine one can, even there, be a Jew of exile. We want to change all this – you know what I mean – and one by himself is too weak to change things. I would like to see Baruch and Levy coming with us. We are getting older – oh, don't laugh, you ungracious wretches! – playing and dreaming can no longer satisfy us. I think Reuben and his friends have done the right thing'. (Reuben half-thought he saw her blushing at the mention of his name – and as for himself, he just wanted to give her a good hug – but that could not be at the moment). 'And now goodbye to all of you – I shall keep a look-out for your ships.'

The last sentence came out with some difficulty, chokingly. Chick must have felt like blubbering, and she jumped straight into the circle of her pals, who pressed round her and screened her from outside curiosity. Reuben felt better after her speech, since he believed that from now onwards the solid core would come forward and he believed in the soundness of that core.

Before the assembly had recovered from the stir caused by Chick's farewell, a new wave of surprise swept the crowd: for Levy had given the word to Eleazar, popularly known as Crusoe on account of his Robinsonian escapades and physique. He was well-known in the movement, but as for making speeches, who had ever heard of such a thing? Reuben could scarcely believe his eyes when he saw Crusoe, with his lumbering gait, barrel chest, and blond Tarzan locks dangling over his brow, actually climbing the speakers' stand: his sleeveless shirt revealed a pair of powerful biceps, and along his wide mouth and boxer's chin played an embarrassed smile or twitch – which of the two was not clear. But on the whole the crowd beneath felt more embarrassed than Crusoe himself; all felt pity for that good, naïve son of a wainwright, who was on the verge of making a fool of himself. Many lowered their eyes in order not to witness the humiliation of a good honest soul. The opening words of Crusoe, spoken robustly in juicy Yiddish, betrayed no nervousness. He stood there clinging to his note-book as if it were the smoothing-adze, with which he was more intimately acquainted.

'I felt no difficulty in following Baruch's speech', Reuben was startled to hear him say. 'He is a master of thought and of the spoken word, as I am a master of the adze and plough. Is it not the tragedy of our people that for over two thousand years they have been dealing in old clothes, greasy money, and ancient words; instead of handling good fine scented timber, and fat solid clods? I envy the learned their wisdom, and enjoy sitting at the feet of the scholar. But alas, we have so many scholars, and too few to sit at their feet. Baruch is not concerned with the question of who grows the fine bread for him, who weaves his cloth and who prints his book. That seems so trivial to Baruch the Man. But I am just an ignorant and coarse-grained fellow, and have had to deal from babyhood with horse-shoeing and broken-down peasant carts. I have been taught by the horsewhip to look sharp for things on the ground; one look to the skies, and a kick of a horse would have sent me flying into the fourth dimension of which Levy spoke the other day. I saw therefore – and this Baruch could not have seen in his books and the heavens – I saw Rumanian peasants bringing us our bread, Ukrainian navvies digging our wells, Poles tanning our leather, and German masons building our houses. Your fathers – I don't condemn them, as many of you wrongly do – sit in their shops to barter the toil of others for a pinch of salt, or run like madmen round the bourse to do "business". Before I came to the convention, Torch showed me a book – what is the name of the writer, Torch?'

Torch's voice came thundering back, 'Dr. Ruppin, Crusoe, on "The Economy of the Jews".'

'Well, that bloke, Dr. Ruppin, has drawn two pyramids. One pyramid stands normally on its base, called peasants, followed by a narrower layer of industrial workers, and so on to the point on the top, marked intellectual workers. He calls that pyramid "normal economy". The other pyramid stands on its head, and Dr. Ruppin calls it "Jewish economy", which any blast of wind brings toppling down. I understand that Dr. Ruppin is also a scholar, and yet nevertheless he maintains that we must change the topsy-turvy position of our economy, and that can be done only by new colonisation in Palestine.

'I want to apologise for my ungainly tongue-wagging. You have probably heard the story told by J. L. Perez. A Jewish lumberjack from the Carpathian forest – there are such blessed folks among us Jews – happened to spend a Sabbath in town. He went to the synagogue: but whereas he was used to a humble synagogue made of timber, he found himself now inside a magnificent building, its dome reaching to the skies, crowded with Jews dressed in curiously-shaped top hats, silk and fine cloth. He heard the voices of cherubim (a choir of children, probably, screened in the gallery), and our lumberjack felt terribly excited. He had never seen such splendour before, and he wanted badly to join with the choir. He did not know the prayers, and loth to remain mute, he put two fingers between tongue and teeth, and gave out a shrill ear-piercing whistle. The consternation of the fine gentlemen may well be imagined. Who ever heard of such a desecration of the House of God? It would have gone badly with our backwoodsmen, had it not been for a wise Rabbi. The wizened old man went up to the lumberman, and putting his hand on the wild man's shoulder, said: "God bless you, pious man. Your way of prayer is just as good, if not better than ours". ". . . I hope", concluded Crusoe, now thoroughly exhausted, and with perspiration dripping down his nose, "that you also will excuse my uncouth whistle".'

Crusoe, slightly dazed and shaky from his effort, removed himself, and quietly shrank into the furthest corner of the barn. Reuben just managed to squeeze his arm as Crusoe slipped past him.

From the mass of characters and speeches Reuben showered on me, I could have filled a book the size of a Hansard Annual. I had to explain to Reuben that such a volume would be incongruous with the general style of my book. He wagged his head, and remarked what a pity that so much good material should be thrown away. But it was quite easy for him to press on me the introduction of Deb – short for Deborah. I liked the character myself and according to Reuben she represented a certain section of opinion in the movement, and he did not want to have the picture of that momentous convention 'cooked'.

Deb was a reddish wisp of a girl. She liked to be taken as dying of consumption, though for the life of him Reuben could not see her dying, even at eighty. She was under five feet high, with a fiery, rosy complexion, crowned by a mop of unruly red-golden hair . . . a type common amongst certain Polish Jews.* A pair of cat-green eyes gazed out from above a perfect nose, and her brilliant rose-red mouth was never at rest. A good orator, quick-witted, with a taste for Bohemian style, Deb was a member of a most unusual family. She never went to school, properly speaking; but considering that her family, from father downwards, was a

---

* Converts to Judaism in South Russia in the 8th—10th centuries.

walking encyclopædia, it was not surprising that she never lacked in willing, though blaspheming, tutors. Her father and his five sons represented big business, poetry, chemical research, the stage, communist agitation and scholarship: while Deb herself was a budding novelist. On a winter night, when her friends gathered in her room in their spacious, crazily noisy house, she would read to them from her as yet unpublished works. The same Deb, clad in a riot of colours, shod in dainty sandals, and with a tiny lace handkerchief in her hand, now climbed leisurely to the speakers' stand.

'Had I not known you', she opened, with a sweetly malicious smile, 'I should have concluded that I had fallen in with nuns and monks, if one ever saw such a meeting en masse. There has been enough sentimental outpouring here to fill all the cavities of the earth. First comes Baruch, going off like a comet on his lonely, lawless adventure. What Baruch actually stands badly in need of is a sound thrashing, preferably by Socrates' wife. Every Socrates, to my way of thinking, rightly deserves his Xantippe. Chick dissolves in tears, and good old Crusoe goes off whistling in a synagogue. There must be something basically wrong with us. I believe that there is too much mysticism and saintliness, and not enough common sense, in our movement. There is too much romanticism, and not enough sound economic and historical knowledge. For the sake of self-protection we withdraw from the world, and now we are paying for it with a high degree of ignorance of the most elementary things. Let us get down to realities! We all agree that the world round us is rotten. Well, what is the reason for it? There is no need to go two thousand years back, or run careering off into astronomic spheres to find the answer. The trouble is that everyone sees only his own little corner. You talk of Jew-baiting, and say we are hated by all the world. Can anyone tell me who is not the object of hatred in our sweet civilization? Germans hate Englishmen, and French, Germans, Rumanians hate Hungarians and Poles Ukrainians. Workers hate capitalists and capitalists hate the blue-blooded aristocracy. Is there an end to it? Children are oppressed by their parents and flogged by their teachers; women are confined to kitchens and child-production, and love is to be bought over the counter. There is overflowing plenty for the one, and nothing for others: and under such circumstances, Baruch speaks of Man, and Crusoe of a pyramid! Can't you see Crusoe, that the whole world is upside-down, and not only the economy of the Jews? For a general trouble there must be a general cause. As for myself, I am convinced that the trouble lies in the capitalistic régime, and that only a social revolution on the Russian standard can mend matters. I don't deny the Palestine solution for those who prefer it, since free migration is a necessary prerequisite for any readjustment of population, under any régime.

I would like our movement to focus attention on a general socialist education, though I admit that the particular Jewish angle deserves consideration. We have done well to keep party politics out of our life so far, and I am in favour of keeping our movement entirely independent. But we "Workers" should divest ourselves of our egocentricity, and actively serve a social ideal. Any stagnation in our political development would land us in medievalism, but, alas! without the fine taste medievalism had for worldly pleasures, which I am afraid our bunch of naïve monks and nuns will never learn!'

A spasm of coughing – a very artistic performance, Reuben thought – indicated the end of her turn. But Deb seemed in no hurry to vanish into the crowd, for she proceeded to chat with the leaders on the platform, informing herself on the success of her performance. I am afraid she found many smiles, but little approval.

With that we shall leave the Convention in general, and turn to Reuben, for the time of his testing had come.

III

When Levy called on Reuben, on the evening of the third day of the deliberations, the convention was close to its end. About thirty delegates had taken part in the debate, and a guess could be made as to the final issue. Baruch, representing the mystics and the cosmopolitan view, had but few adherents: and yet they had a powerful standing in the movement. Some of the cleverest and most authoritative leaders belonged to this party, and their view had been law in the movement for many years. Deborah's international socialist views, coupled with a rather offensive tolerance towards the Palestine 'infatuation', had as yet only a small following: but it was strong and influential as a result of the coherent logic of their programme and the chance it offered of

immediate adventurous action. However, the mass of the delegates were Zionist, and ardently pro-Palestine: but to my surprise,
Reuben classed them – paradoxically, I thought – as the greatest
danger to the movement.

'Didn't you want them to be Zionist and pro-Palestine?' I
asked.

'Of course, but the attitude of the majority fairly reeked of a
sort of Zionism you unfortunately find among Jews in many parts
of the world. It has been defined by a wit as the programme in
which one Jew tries to persuade another Jew to give money for a
third Jew – a *schnorrer* – to emigrate to Palestine. They were
Zionist because they knew they were Jews, some by religion, but
all by blood and nationality. But as to the responsibilities which
went with Zionism; demanding the realisation of their profession
of faith in deeds, they were somewhat vague. Those who followed
Baruch and Deb, on the other hand, were strongly idealistic, and
ready for any sacrifice that should be demanded of them by their
ideals. My task was therefore not to lose the qualitatively higher
idealism of mystics and international socialists; but at the same
time to make clear to the Zionist youngsters that they were not
asked for a complacent patriotic lip-service, but for a revolution
in their personal way of life.

It was my object to show the adventurous idealists that the
opportunities offered by a communal life, based on hard manual
labour, and on new social and spiritual values, was in fact superior
to anything they might find in any philosophy, or in a radical
movement in Europe. I am glad to say that the attempt was not
entirely unsuccessful, thereby preserving for our future work a
group of people who lent it drive and uncompromising action.
That group once freed from the pursuit of abstract interna-
tionalism, came bursting into the inertia of the majority, and
whirled them into the lasting adventure of production, of return
to the soil, and of collective life, as developed by our settlements
in Palestine.

'What were your fundamental principles, Reuben?'

'Our programme was to extricate the personality of the individual from the clogging of civilization around about him. We
wanted to develop all the uniqueness of the individual man. I still
think that as an educational first objective, there is nothing finer.
Baruch and his like refused to accept this as a merely educational
principle, and insisted on having it as a lifetime ideal – the self-

contained Man. It is obvious that the mass of the movement was
quite incapable of climbing such heights of individual discipline.
We were all social animals if you like, and moreover with a very
keen appreciation of our obligations to our own people, and
through them, to mankind. I therefore made an attempt to eluci-
date this point to the convention, namely that the task of a youth
movement is to clear all obstacles which hinder the individual
from serving man. You see, I did not aim at a personality in
empty space, but at a personality and individual character vitally
dependent on, and of service to, the community. I believe that in
the end the convention endorsed that view, and incorporated it
among the principles of the youth movement.

'The other principle, which aroused conflict in our young
brains – as it still does in the wide world generally – was the
sincere longing for an intimate relationship with all men, trans-
cending such partitions as race, religion, and nationality. I want
you Jack, to understand one of the main reasons why that ideal
had at all times a very strong influence upon us Jews. My theory
is that when our divorce from country, and national and political
life came to be regarded as an irretrievable fact, it was easier for
the Jew of the Diaspora to embrace cosmopolitan ideals than
purely national ones. After all, for a time the Jew was a stranger
and an alien wherever he went. His stay in a particular country
and among a definite national group was never quite certain. At
any time he might have to move on to a new country. Well, can't
you see it? Instead of embracing year by year, or generation after
generation, the ideals, beliefs and idols of new countries, he made
a short cut and created an ideal embracing them all in one sweep,
in the imaginary international unit, mankind! This made life
psychologically easier, for it served the purpose of providing the
wandering, migrating Jew with a facile answer to the embarrassing question: "Who and what are you?" "I am a citizen of
the world to come, of the brotherhood of all men!" comes back
the answer of Ahasuerus.

'Having such a background with which to contend, it was
essential to drive home to my friends two things: first that our
national and political life was not irretrievably lost . . . indeed,
through Zionism and the Balfour Declaration we had been given
an internationally affirmed opportunity to retrieve it; secondly,
that the shortest way to a closer international relationship was
through an ever-developing co-operation between national

entities, and impossible of attainment by atomised, nondescript globe-trotters. Consequently, our only chance to bring to fruition our ideal of a future brotherhood of man, was through the medium of our own rehabilitated national group and home. I believe that this point was also carried by a large majority of the convention.

'After these matters had been cleared up, there still remained Deb's strong appeal, an appeal such as would fall on fertile ground among any post-revolution generation . . . the appeal for socialist action. That was also in the nature of a psychological short-cut. Well, try and feel yourself in our position, Jack, and don't look so puzzled: the position was that we all felt morally shaken by the way our fathers, uncles, brothers, made their money. We lived on that money, studied in universities, talked of the brotherhood of man, of equity, liberty, morality, and so on. All this was made possible for us through the money of our people. The conscience of our crowd was uneasy about it. Of this there was no doubt – as far as we, the superior young revolutionaries were concerned – such money was not clean. It came from business exploitation, speculation, and from all those other practices which are the source of individual wealth. These were anathema to us all. Deb and her pals provided a very plausible and moreover a very convenient answer. We shall be socialists, they said, and fight for a new society. As long as such society is not established, things must go on as they are – nobody can help that. In the meantime, we ourselves are becoming doctors, lawyers, journalists, all on the proceeds of corrupt money: is it logical to accept the benefits of it and yet fight for a new order? After all, what can one do more than that, while the régime is unregenerate, without coming into ill-repute as a utopian or a Don Quixote? You see what I mean by the term short-cut? One can go on striving privately on money amassed by capitalistic methods, and yet fight for socialism, thereby quieting one's conscience. I think this was a trap for us, and I am afraid it still is for large sections of our gilded youth: had our movement fallen into it, it would have perished in the mire of hypocrisy.

'Against Deb's ingenious contention we had the powerful weapon forged for us by our Chaluzim (pioneers, advanced guard) in Palestine. Instead of fighting for socialism, while living as national and social parasites, they became, first of all, manual labourers and peasants living by their own toil. Secondly, instead of proclaiming a theoretical new order for the future, they went and built an actual new social order for themselves, in collective settlements. There was no doubt that for a sincere Jewish youth there could be no true alternative. All I had to do at the convention was to hammer that in to counter any cosmopolitan socialist hankerings of the Jewish youth. If socialism does not mean, for those who embrace it, in the first instance, living on one's own work without exploiting the work of others, and next – whenever the opportunity may be found – building a society based on collective principles – what then is socialism? The Jewish youth had been given a most unusual historical opportunity, not only to talk socialism, but to carry it out. And in so doing they would revolutionise their own life and that of their people, before attempting to revolutionise the lives of others. This we called Hagshamah ("actualisation", practising what one preaches). Even Deb had to give in: and I must say this for her, she gave in graciously, and became a most valuable member of our new executive. Yet others remained aloof; eventually left our movement and went their ways.

'Once agreed that nationally and socially our way was to be "Creative Palestine",' proceeded Reuben with glee, 'it became obvious that such a movement could only be led by people who were ready to practise it. It was a movement asking a high price of the individual, and there was as yet no Hitler to help us to make up our minds. The individual would have to leave wealth and comfortable bourgeois conditions, and go as a manual labourer to Palestine. Unlike many other moral or revolutionary movements, we had an instrument for testing the honesty of our adherents. It was not possible to talk one's way out of personal moral obligations. The test was the Hagshamah, the personal act of going in for hard manual training, and living in a social community based on mutual help and assistance.

'For the execution of such a programme, the movement had to elect its leaders from people who would practise what they preached. A few of the old leaders like Torch, Lea, Deb and others, went with us. But most of the members of the new leadership were people who had already stood such a test. I found myself among them; and very soon new responsibilities of leadership devolved upon me. The new leadership inaugurated the future course of the movement, and opened the era of Hagshamah.'

As the tale of the convention unfolded itself, it became clear that it would help the reader to obtain an insight into the problems with which Reuben and his generation were at grips. It certainly explained to me many aspects of the new collective work in Palestine, which before had appeared to be somewhat artificial. It made also for a better understanding of Reuben's character, and his way of looking at the problems of my own country. It had often irked me, whenever we came to discuss 'Better Britain', to hear Reuben's whisper, 'What are you, Jack, and all the Jacks, going to do personally for the change?' But I readily forgave him when I heard the story of the convention, and the decisions he had made himself.

CHAPTER THREE

LEADERSHIP

I

WITH THE ALLIED forces approaching the Western frontiers of the Reich, the Brunswick area came more and more within the zone of the Allied air-fleets. Our confidence in the immunity of our camp had been badly shaken, and we took to the shelter of the basement whenever the 'red' alarm went. As our 'planes extended the length of their attacks from the original thirty minutes to some raids of five hours on end, we came to linger in the basement, or in close proximity to it, for a good part of the day and night. No systematic work or study was to be thought of under such circumstances, but there was plenty of scope for conversation. Any topic – except modern air warfare – was welcome. So we chatted while pacing the long passage of the basement, or ascending to the front of our houses when the waves of bombers had passed overhead; always ready to withdraw should necessity arise.

Most of the present chapter in Reuben's life was pieced together from such snippets of conversation. It took me about eight days to compile, so often were we rudely interrupted. I doubt whether I have made a success of it, since both the talking and the writing had to be done under circumstances not exactly conducive to concentrated thought. Both of us – Reuben and myself – showed marked signs of agitation and restlessness whenever the wail of the German sirens came crooning over us.

The question may well be asked by post-war psychologists, how the German people stood such a nerve-racking strain for so long. We at least had the satisfaction of knowing that the bombs, mines and incendiaries were not directed against us; but every German knew they were intended to bring destruction to his factories, home, and life itself. We often wondered how the Germans in Ruhr and Rhine, Berlin and Hamburg areas, managed to carry on their work and routine life after thousands of tons of explosive had repeatedly come down upon them. The fact that concentration camps, lunatic asylums or the gallows were kept ready by the Gestapo to receive all those, men or women, who failed to keep their nerve or hold their tongues, cannot account satisfactorily for this phenomenon of 'sticking it'. The high morale and steadfastness displayed by our people during the 'blitz' on England cannot be taken as an analogous case. Our people knew they were defended by the R.A.F.: though few in numbers, they were untiringly overhead. Moreover, there was no comparison between the weight, speed and terror of our raids, with those of the Germans over England. The investigating psychologist may well come to the conclusion that the answer to this investigation lies outside his competence: for we came to doubt whether he would find any psychological reaction amongst the people of the Nazi Reich! We P's.O.W. often wondered whether our gaolers, and the people to whom they belonged, had anything in them justifying the use of a psychological terminology. Such an analysis was not dictated to us by depreciation of the German character, but offered itself to us as a result of experience and immediate contact. We often felt pity for a nation which within one decade had come down to such low standards of individual self-determination. Personal feeling and judgment appeared to us to have been uprooted by the state machinery; and the propaganda picture of the robot-race appeared to us to be much nearer the mark than any other less crude, analytical definition.

By making such a digression from my subject, I don't intend to put forward any excuse for our own crankiness. We were certainly jittery, when the roaring 'express trains' shook our buildings, and when wave after wave of our bombers went in to attack an objective within a mile or two of our camp. As we got used to it, and when the intervals between the attacks on our area allowed of it, I renewed my conversations with Reuben. I found it a good means of escaping from present actuality into more soothing spheres.

And so one morning, pacing the concrete run in front of our bungalow, I asked Reuben to tell me what had happened to him and the movement, after the convention was over.

'As the tale of the convention spread, with the reports delivered by the delegates', began Reuben, casting a glance at the condensation-trails overhead, 'our boys and girls must have felt the change deeply. Baruch, Levy, and many more of the young people's heroes had resigned: and there was a feeling of bereavement. We, the young new members of the headquarters, had yet to make

97

our mark, and there was much talk of "dogmatic new leaders!"
We also had some difficulty in making our friends take up the
full-time duties at headquarters. Just then there were only four or
five people required for it; but each of us wanted to get on with
his manual training. We settled it at last: and I managed to be
left out, and could proceed with my schemes. I took upon myself
the management of the training department, as I thought it best
to do that part of our work from a communal centre in one of our
working groups. There was a considerable influx of people to our
working communities, and new stations on farms had to be found
for them. My own group had increased during the convention
from eight to twenty-six members, and we had to look out for a
new location. We also had it in mind to try a new system of
training, and I was fortunate enough to take the lead in it.

'The six months' training, preceding the convention, which we
had completed on the agricultural estate on the upper Pruth, was
by no means a joke. The owner of the estate – a rich Jewish land-
holder, of whom there were many in the area – thought it a great
idealistic sacrifice to take us on at all. He paid us in kind, a bare
minimum of coarse food. It was quite insufficient to appease the
appetites of young, growing, and hard-working animals of our
type. We worked from sunrise to sunset, and yet were never free
from the pangs of hunger. Our staple food consisted of potatoes,
maize porridge, vegetables, and a pint of milk each day. Meat
came our way only on Saturdays – our rest day. And what with
blisters, and other acclimatisation illnesses, life was hard. Nevertheless, we felt it to be somewhat too secure and sheltered, and
scarcely approaching the envisaged demands of the labour market
in Palestine. We knew that in the orange plantations we would
have to face the competition of the cheap and hardy Arab
labourer, and that the contractors for the drying of swamps and
building of roads expected a high standard of output. The
question presented itself, whether we should not find some work
more closely akin to conditions in the open labour market there,
than was offered by our present agricultural estate.

'The idea was to go to some town and see what figure we
should cut when confronted by old-time labourers whose grandfathers were themselves the descendants of manual labourers.
We were not quite free to choose where. Firstly, all places where
our parents lived were barred to us. Most of us had broken off
relations with our families when we refused to follow family

traditions, and we felt no inclination to have our lives and work spoilt by taking up employment in our home towns. The other difficulty was to find a place where work was to be obtained without encroaching on the interests of the native labourers, whether organised or not.

'We eventually chose a town in Northern Bessarabia for my group, as well as several other places on the lower Dniester for the remainder. My own group went to B., a county capital with a population of about 100,000 souls, of whom about half were Jews. We found there a few oil presses, which even in that land of cheap and unorganised labour, suffered from lack of workers, as a result of the appalling hygienic and social conditions prevailing in that primitive industry. The presses worked day and night, in two shifts. Wages were so low that even though we were all single, and with all of us boys and girls working, we could not subsist on them. The other work at hand was wood-chopping, for firewood was the only fuel in use in that province. The firewood used to arrive by rail, in four-foot logs, and was then brought to the yards of the citizens in carts. Parties of four wood-choppers, equipped with cross-cut saws and axes, used to follow these carts to their various destinations. There they would take on jobs at a fixed price per cubic metre.

We acquired the necessary equipment, and after some parley with the native wood-choppers, we were admitted into the guild. We soon realised that the agreed price was revoltingly low, and saw no reason why the good citizens should get away with it. I tried discussions with my native colleagues – all very simple and superstitious Greek orthodox proletarians – but with no appreciable success. They were suspicious of us: for they were content and wanted no trouble. So we made up our minds to force their hands. One morning the native wood-chopper gangs, waiting in the town square for the carts to drive by, must have been surprised by the absence of our party. The same morning I went down to the railway station and made a copy of the consignment invoice. So before the carts were loaded, I was back with the list of addresses and had despatched my parties to those houses which had ordered firewood. When the native parties duly arrived in the wake of the carts, they found our people all set for the task. They looked puzzled at such wizardry, and without more ado crossed themselves. At last, after this trick was repeated on the second day, the explanation of the miracle dawned on them. This time they refrained from crossing themselves, and turned on us with their axes. What a devilish Judas-treachery they cried, but as we showed no signs of being frightened by their onslaught, they had to sit down with us and discuss matters. I now had it my own way: but alas! this, my first attempt at the organisation of Labour, was a humiliating failure.

'I sat down with Vassily, the brightest brain of the native lumberjacks, in a tea-house, to discuss our drive for better prices.

' "Well, Vassily", I addressed his pock-marked stubble face, from which the left eye had been cleanly gouged out in some brawl, as he proudly boasted. "Let us come to terms. Are you really satisfied with the price paid for the cutting, chopping and storing of the firewood?"

' "I am well content with my lot, praised be the Lord!" Vassily replied, making the sign of the Cross, "though to tell you the truth, I don't make enough to have vodka for myself and medicines for my children. It is something awful how the price of vodka and medicines goes up. But what can we do?"

' "Can't you see, Vassily," I explained patiently, "there is no need for us to live without meat and butter, or for your children to be without medicines. The citizens for whom we chop the firewood can well afford to pay a higher price, without even noticing it."

' "Ha, ha!" whinnied Vassily, "those Jews (most of our customers were Jews) have certainly bags of money. But how can we make them pay more? They are as shrewd as seven Satans, and they will always get the better of us."

' "Look here, Vassily," I said to him, "I am also a Jew, and I tell you if we all refuse to cut wood for less than 20 lei a cubic metre, they can do nothing! They must have wood; we are willing to chop it . . . provided they pay the price. If we remain firm and united, we must win!"

'Vassily spat a good deal, scratched his back, wiped the perspiration from his brow with his sleeves, and eventually agreed that the plan was good, and that I must have been sent down by the Lord himself to better the lot of the wood-choppers . . . although, to the end, he remained puzzled as to the object of Jewish gentlemen becoming wood-choppers.

'When the new prices were presented to the citizens next morning by each party in turn, they first mocked at them, and then became alarmed. Those new funny intellectuals masquerading as wood-choppers, were a menace, wolves in sheep's clothing, enemies of private property, in short, Bolsheviki. The same Vassily was taken into confidence by a few citizens, and enlightened about the trap he had fallen into. Should he refuse to dissociate himself from us, they told him, the matter would have to be brought to the notice of the Sigurantza (Rumanian Gestapo). That settled Vassily and his crowd . . . and made a swift end to my Trade Union. In place of getting better prices, we had to kowtow for work . . . for, after all, that was the first thing we had to think about. The wood-choppers shunned us from then onwards like the plague, and life proceeded in the good old rut as before.'

'You surely could have managed to get some financial support for your training schemes?' I argued with Reuben. 'Greenhorns as you were, you surely had no hope of making a living by your own unaided work!' I had, after so many talks, become fairly familiar with the idea of 'productive labourisation' and the return to manual work, as preached and practised by Reuben and his friends. 'But why', I asked, 'such a ruthless method of acquiring it, surely it could have been achieved under less severe conditions.'

'You should make no mistake about our method!' reiterated Reuben, who was sensitive on this point, 'we might have been hopelessly romantic in many other respects, but as regards the method of our training we approached our task with stark realism. You have been to the Near East, and must have seen for yourself the social conditions which prevail there. It is rather different to-day, particularly in the Jewish economic sector: but we had to be prepared to face the competition of cheap un-organised labour, which was tremendously favoured by the class of Jewish plantation-owners who cared first and foremost for profit. Before a community could pass through the wilderness to a promised land of its own, on which to build its settlement, many years had to be spent by the members working as hired labour on capitalistic plantations, or on public works under Government management. Here the social status of the Jewish labourer was lowered to that of the Arab. We had already had some contact with labour-conditions in Palestine, and were under no illusions as to the struggle awaiting us there. So we had to put ourselves through a rigorous grounding to avoid disillusionment and crises later on. I must not forget to remind you that the test was not merely one of physical fitness. Above all we had to find out for ourselves whether we were capable of living as a community under adverse economic circumstances. The true social test for the individual – as you, Jack, a P.O.W. will certainly agree – comes when there is not enough bread to go round; when you have to give up your good bunk for a sick man to lie in; when unemployment makes you listless and irritable; in short, conditions under which character is the key to survival. Our ideal was not only to become workers, but also to build a new social unit on collective principles. Only a very realistic environment could serve the purpose of proving ourselves and our fellows. The ideal was professed and believed in by all of us. We wished to know whether we had succeeded in forming our characters and life accordingly. The answer could not be found in words or speeches but only through actual experience. Of the twenty-five members of our group for instance, four left us to return to their homes and old ways of life.'

My curiosity was aroused. 'I should like to hear more about those four people who returned home', I said to Reuben. 'How did they fail?'

'I am surprised at the interest you appear to take in such abstruse experiences – I mean abstruse from your point of view, Jack.

'Take the case of Jehu. He belonged to the circle of our most intellectual friends. An excellent speaker, and an untiring propagandist for Zionism and the labourisation of the Jewish people. He prided himself on being a radical in these matters, and had we acted on his advice, we should have had to expel from the movement all those who failed to leave home at a certain age, and take up some sort of manual training. He had to put himself to the test and joined our group. He was physically a normal type of youngster, who had grown up in comfortable bourgeois surroundings. He made a good and sincere effort for the first fortnight or so, and mastered the technique of woodcutting quite satisfactorily. Then suddenly he began to drop out; nondescript illnesses, melancholia, claim for the special food ration reserved for sick people, and so on. At last he made a clean breast of it, and admitted that his strength of character failed him. The ideals of our life were beyond praise; but he could not live up to them. He had never realised that this sort of life would require such a physical and spiritual effort, and that the habits of selfishness and personal comfort gained at the expense of others, were so deeply rooted in him. He did not, as often happened, blame us for his failure; went back to continue the study of law, and eventually emigrated to South America, where he has doubtless made a name for himself as a defender of the rights of the people, and of the common good.

'Then there was the case of Fanny, whose mother was the widow of a millionaire. She became an excellent member of our community. Fanny was hard working, devoted to the comforts of others: worked as a housemaid, and later, at gardening in a tree nursery. She was a mistress of improvisation, and managed to furnish our dilapidated slum-quarters, making them look homely and keeping them spotlessly clean. Fanny had a very fine voice, and trilled happily while she scrubbed floors, or mended socks. She was happy and contented as never before in her life. Then, one unpleasant day in winter, her mother arrived at our quarters. She was a handsome woman, cloaked in furs and feathers, sporting plenty of jewels on her podgy white fingers. On coming in, she embraced her daughter demonstratively, and was just as fulsomely sentimental with the other girls. She paid tremendous compliments on the tidiness of our humble quarters, and finally asked her daughter to accompany her to a teashop for a private conversation. When they eventually returned I was sitting at the table with a bowl of maize porridge in front of me. I was startled by Fanny's face, which showed signs of carefully dried tears; she came up to me, and laying a trembling hand on my shoulder whispered into my ear that Mamma would like to have a chat with me. We went into a cubicle which served as the office. Fanny kept close to her mother. A conversation followed of a type well known to me from many previous occasions. The gist of it was that Mamma was anxious to have her youngest and dearest daughter with her; and the daughter, although strong enough to flaunt all family claims upon her, capitulated in face of Mamma's sentimental and selfish appeal. Fanny left us the same day; and in the course of a few months, true to the prediction I made before she left, she was married off to a lawyer of Mamma's own choice. Fanny never forgot to send us sundry knick-knacks and cakes, whenever her regrets – or her conscience – troubled her. It took her a long time to forget. There is no need to go any further on this topic', Reuben chuckled, 'as all break-downs were either of Fanny's or Jehu's type.'

II

On two successive days no opportunity offered itself to record Reuben's story. The almost continuous air-raid alarms, and the unprovoked murder of an Indian officer by a German sentry made the task of writing appear quite out of place. The Indian officer had been playing a game of deck tennis on a court adjoining the trip wire, 'On crossing or touching of which, the sentry will shoot without challenge' – ran the warning of the German Commandant. The Indian officer neither touched, nor crossed, the trip-wire. All he did was to bend down, in order to pick up the quoit ring from the ground. The sentry box was about twenty yards to the North of it. The sentry, a young Nazi, put his rifle to his shoulder and aimed straight at the forehead of the Indian officer. His skull was shattered, and many experts believed that the sentry used a dum-dum round. There were many witnesses about, among them a German N.C.O. who had the courage to call the sentry a murderer. The German Commandant promised to carry out an impartial enquiry. Thus, what with one thing and another, I had no mind to take notes and must now rely entirely on my memory.

I gathered that during that winter Reuben had to dodge several efforts made to entice him to take up his post at H.Q. But there was still important work to be done before he could feel free to take up the formal leadership of the movement. His long-cherished dream of acquiring a training farm, seemed at last to be within his reach. According to Reuben, they would never have gained this object but for the appearance of one Stenka on the scene. I took to Stenka as soon as I had heard Reuben's first description of him.

Stenka was a nickname bestowed on this fellow by friend and foe alike, in memory of the Ukrainian Robin Hood, Stenka Razin. He came with a crowd of Jewish youngsters over the Dniester from Russia. The Russian Jews represented, I understood, a quite different type from those organised by Reuben's movement. They were not the pampered, polished, striplings of a hothouse, but were a growth of the vigorous unorganised Russian life. Most of them were students of Russian universities, and belonged to the revolutionary intellectual circles, whose battle cry was, 'Back to the people', as first proclaimed by the Tolstoian school. They did not flee Russia in the dead of night, enfiladed by Russian and Rumanian M.G. fire, because of any feelings of antagonism toward the new Bolshevik régime. They had no quarrel with Bolshevism, but the Russian Government, under pressure brought to bear by Jewish communists, suddenly declared Zionism to be a reactionary movement, whose main *raison d'être* was to assist in the establishment of British Imperialism in the Near East. Large sections of the Jewish Youth in Russia had had deep affinities with Zionism and Palestine, in fact Russian Jewry had been from the start a mainstay of the Palestine reconstruction work. As against the Jewish communists, who advocated an assimilation policy of the individual to the majority people among whom they happened to find themselves, the Zionist youth adhered to the idea of labourisation as an integral part of the political and national Jewish renaissance in Palestine. As long as the Russian Government misinterpreted their ideals, there was nothing left to them but to leave the country illegally, and to make their way to Palestine as best they could. The Rumanian and Polish governments, though officially opposed to the illegal crossing of their frontiers, agreed grudgingly to grant temporary permits for the emigrants, until emigration-certificates for Palestine had been procured for them.

Stenka was one of their leading figures who had organised the young refugees into a strong organisation, 'Hechalutz' (The Pioneer) in order to provide training facilities for Palestine. As the 'Workers' of Reuben's organisation had the same ideal, both groups united for the sake of developing and advancing the Zionist Labourisation movement among the Jewish youth. Stenka, although an illegal refugee and stranger, had rapidly made a name for himself in the country. He was at home in all circles of local Jewry, and maintained also, by indirect means, good contacts with the authorities. He achieved his standing, not by diplomacy, but by sheer force of character. Stenka proclaimed himself a Tolstoian. This meant for him, in practice, a frank disgust for western civilization; he was an extreme vegetarian, and washed himself at infrequent intervals to express his contempt for the soft vanities; he would sleep on a bench or table, as he considered beds to be too dainty for him. A pair of breeches, tucked into Russian top boots which had never made the acquaintance of boot-polish, a Russian tunic, a huge military great coat and a

traveller's cap sufficed for him sartorially. He changed his outfit
only when his underwear began to peep through holes. His face
was lean and long, but one seldom saw more of it than his jutting-
out powerful chin, and a pair of grey-green cat-eyes, which bored
hypnotically into those of his fellow-men. He spoke little; when
he did, he seemed rather to hiss, but he preferred to bang his fist
on the table as a means of expression.

As Reuben sat on the board of the united 'Pioneers' he had to
endure a great deal from Stenka's mulishness, for nobody ever
managed to get him to change his views. Officially he would
submit to the decision of the board; but if he were left to handle
a matter, he always did it according to his own lights. He was a
one track man, fanatical in his principles, hatreds and loves. As
usual with such characters he was terribly sentimental. He was
known to have wept bitter tears when he witnessed the crushing
of a stray kitten by a motor-car. Reuben believed that he lived
entirely by his instincts and senses, for he had a violent loathing
and mistrust of intellectual quibbles. Stenka's motto became
famous:

'What you feel and sense, is the fundamental reaction of your
being! What you believe to be Reason is merely a Hollywood production of the trickster "Brain". No brainy stuff for me, please,
I am not afraid of the truth', was his usual form of repartee to
ideological argument.

This same Stenka had been working on a scheme of his own to
get a farm, as he did not believe that such a thing could be
achieved by the deliberations of committees. So he had set out
to find one, following his own lone-wolf methods. The way he
set about acquiring this farm is better told in Reuben's own
words:

'There is no better example of Stenka's character and the
methods employed by him', replied Reuben to my queries, 'than
the way he "bought" our farm. As a start he picked two rich
Jews, who, in his opinion, were destined by providence to provide
us with a farm. One, a gentleman whom Stenka named Brilliant,
was very rich, with no heirs, and no charity in his heart. Gentleman "B" had many sins to atone for – mused Stenka, he would
offer him a chance of salvation. If gentleman "B" had the fear of
God in his heart, he would fall on his knees and offer thanks to
Stenka for the chance. If gentleman "B" had none of it, then
Stenka would be morally obliged to force him to pay him, in cash

100,000 Lei. The other benefactor christened Jade, by Stenka, was the owner of many estates. Several of these estates were under cultivation and were flourishing, but there was just one – Stenka had his agents – abandoned, derelict, in short, prostituted in the eyes of God and men. Here Stenka's fist shook the table. He, Stenka, would willingly kill the Gentleman, were he not assured that Jade professed himself a "man of ideals". Well, what is the good of having ideals, hissed Stenka, if you don't realise them?

'Stenka assured me that he saw in me a future leader of the organisation, although I had still to eradicate many traces of intellectualism. These consisted in my all-too-neat attire and pusillanimity regarding ethical blackmail as practised by him! So I had the privilege of accompanying Stenka on his piratical journeys.

'The first visit was to Gentleman B. Stenka telephoned to tell him that two representatives of our organisation would call on him on a very urgent matter. Gentleman B was a fat little man, very agile considering his age and figure, who lived in a little villa outside Kishinev, the capital of Bessarabia. He received Stenka cordially enough, and expressed his satisfaction at my presence, as he felt vaguely uneasy about a tête-à-tête with Stenka. Stenka was as cold as marble – biding his time. Our host invited us to his study, where the indispensable Samovar was in full steam. Having taken our seats, and warmed our cold hands on glasses of tea, Gentleman B asked us to what he owed the pleasure of our visit. Still no word from Stenka. We both looked at him, but he seemed far away in the land of dreams. I feared an explosion, and at that moment it came.

' "Gentleman B! I hope you have done with your idle chatter. I have a good business proposition to make. Gentleman J, whom you probably know," hissed Stenka, "has offered us one of his farms". ('That was surprising news to me, the truth of which I had reason to doubt', interpolated Reuben), "We want money, not much, a paltry 100,000 Lei! You, Gentleman B will kindly make us a donation of the amount required, in any form you choose. If you refuse to make us a gift of it – and this would be quite in line with your miserable character – I shall take the money as a loan and sign any papers you like". (Gentleman B. chuckled). "Don't chuckle!" sizzled Stenka, "it irritates my sensitive ears, which have been given to me to listen to nightingales and Tchaikowsky, and not to the mockery of a moneylender.

100,000 Lei it is, and not a word more!" Gentlemen B. stopped chuckling all right, when he looked up and met Stenka's stern gaze. I cannot recall exactly how things developed, but before long there was shouting, fist-banging, chinking of splintered glass, tea splashing on the table and the ruin of a good Persian carpet, until eventually a grave-yard silence followed.

'It was ended by a burst of laughter from our host and a satisfied grunt from Stenka. Mr. Brilliant declared himself assaulted, in broad daylight, by a robber! How decent old Barczik whom he knew and honoured, could have begotten a son like Stenka – he could not imagine. But at last we put our signatures to a receipt. Gentleman B. insisted on having my name on this as well, and the gift in the form of bundles of banknotes changed hands. Stenka himself refused to touch the filthy money. It was obviously filched from widows and orphans – he cried. So I had to load my pockets with it. I liked Mr. Brilliant's manner, and told him so; the old man was deeply touched by my simple words of gratitude. "You should have been my son", cried Mr. Brilliant, while shaking my hand! "Oh, a son, a son! You, Reuben, may come to me again when you want help; but don't bring Stenka – another visit from him and I shall be finished!"

'Stenka replied coolly that a melodramatic actor of Mr. Brilliant's calibre would outlive us all. With a half smile from Stenka and a "Protect you God!" we took our leave. I thought Mr. Brilliant felt as happy about his loss of money as I felt happy at the gain of it, but as for Stenka, he stumped along at my side with never a word.

'The same evening we left Kishinev for Balti, where Mr. Jade, the landowner, lived. We travelled third class of course, and dared not doze off for fear of pickpockets. There is a saying that on Rumanian trains there are always more pickpockets than passengers. Needless to say, Jack, Stenka refused to deposit the money in a bank, an untrustworthy institution, and as a result we had the banknotes sewn in the underlining of our tunics.

'On arrival in Balti early next morning, Stenka dragged me straight to Mr. Jade's house. I protested in vain against calling on a man at six o'clock in the morning, but to no avail. We drew up in a dilapidated sleigh, looking like two grimy, dishevelled bandits, alighting to rob a victim. Stenka knocked angrily at the door; and the butler, an old Russian with grey locks, crossed himself on coming face to face with two such disreputable visitors.

He was, however, easily conciliated by Stenka, who addressed him in a juicy Russian idiom, and as Stenka was no stranger to the house, we were admitted.

Stenka insisted on going straight to J's bedroom; but the butler vetoed this so firmly that Stenka gave in. J's was a rich bachelor establishment, furnished in an over-pronounced Balkan-Turkish style. There were carpets, cushions, divans, short-legged stools and tables. I asked the butler for a good hot bath. He was delighted to oblige. Stenka, however, refused indignantly to accept the offer of one for himself. As far as I was concerned, it was a heavenly affair after the ramshackle bucket shower at our training quarters. When I came back to the room, I found Gentleman J. in excited conversation with Stenka. I mean Gentleman J. was excited – Stenka was facing him calmly, his eyes boring into his opponent, and maintaining an ominous silence. Gentleman J. was wrapped in a Chinese-pattern dressing-gown. His black hair, greying noticeably at the temples, was heavily pomaded, and he gave the impression of being a real *bon vivant* which in truth he was. As Stenka failed to introduce me, I carried out the formalities myself, while making apologies, and expressing thanks for having enjoyed his bathroom. Gentlemen J. waved aside my thanks, and appealed to me desperately to intervene with Stenka, who was again in one of his mulish moods.

' "Shut up, J.', I heard Stenka say, "Reuben is not familiar with your tricks; but I know what breakfast first, and business next means. I bet you have already ordered your henchmen, and will be called away on urgent affairs as soon as breakfast is over. You might as well know that your pal, Gentleman B., is at this moment in bed, with several doctors fussing about him, because he tried some funny tricks on me. What about that prostitute . . .

"Stenka", ejaculated Gentleman J. in protest.

' "Oh, I don't mean any of your mistresses," proceeded Stenka stiffly, "I referred to the farm where you have prostituted God's good earth. I am willing to pay you 50,000 Lei right now – Reuben has the money on him. Let's get the contract signed at once."

' "You are as mad as a hatter," retorted Gentleman J. dropping on to a divan, "I am completely unable to understand how a maniac of your calibre is free to go round and blackmail honest folk. I have done, and shall continue to do my best for Palestine, but I am damned if I will part with 500 acres of good land and fine apple orchards for a song."

' "O.K.," whispered Stenka, "I shall bring my boys and girls, who are hungry for a bit of land, to wait for your answer here in these whorish surroundings. I shall also send a hundred boys to your derelict farm, so that you may have good reason to call out the police. Come Reuben, let us flee this unholy place!"

'Such extreme measures however, were not to prove necessary. We made out a contract, cut the lining of my tunic, and paid out 50,000 Lei. Then we proceeded to indulge in our best breakfast for a long time, and furthermore obtained an undertaking from Jade to hire 50 of our boys and girls on one of his best run estates. Even Stenka was appeased, and mumbled some benevolent phrases as we took our leave!

'Well, that was Stenka', said Reuben, concluding his sketch of that amazing character.

In my life I have known a fair number of people who have managed to get away with things which would have landed many another man in jail. Nevertheless, I had some difficulty in getting my bearings in the case of Stenka. I was bewildered not so much at Stenka's methods – quite consistent I thought with the methods employed in Russia before and after the revolution – but by the blatantly spineless reaction of the two Gentlemen, his victims, I do not know of any moneyed or landed men who would have submitted to such treatment. Reuben listened to my remarks reflectively, and replied in a tone which betrayed his inner emotion.

'I share your feelings entirely Jack, as that was exactly how I felt after having been an eye witness of the scenes I have just described. These experiences had a profound influence on my future relations with our older generation, for whom I had entertained so far either contempt or pity. I was nevertheless wise enough never to imitate Stenka. Whereas he succeeded by using such methods, another man doing the same would have made a fool of himself. I was surprised not so much by Stenka's character – as by the deep awe in which those hard-boiled businessmen held him. It would be ludicrous to assume that they were afraid of him. Those people were used to blackmailers, and to crooked methods, and knew how to counter them. Stenka however, was accepted by them with unreserved admiration and this is how I interpret their reaction; he represented for them a prototype of that Jewish character which was alive to their unconscious and hidden longings. They had been dealing with many Jewish types who, like themselves, were concerned with their own petty interests and whose aim was only to further their own ends. They had also been used to beggars, charity hunters, sycophants, and other parasites of the rich. They were flattered by these men because they had money. But here, probably for the first time in their experience, came a young Jew, ragged and hungry, himself a refugee but with no thought of feathering his own nest. He did not beg, and did not flatter; instead he told them what he thought of their way of life, and their methods of money-making. He came and demanded tribute for an idealistic cause, which was both theirs and his. They knew that Stenka was right and that they were wrong and they also knew the source of his unmasked brutality. The same conditions which forged a Stenka, had also shaped their own lives. Alas! in their youth there was not much to push and pull them in Stenka's direction. The strong trend of their time had left them with but three main choices: to throw bombs, to commit suicide, or to make money, big money. And they chose the last. Now, having attained their goal, they felt empty and burnt-out. What has it brought us? and what will be the end of such a course? they asked themselves. Stenka, the rock-like, unbending, intolerant, fist-banging personification of the pride of human dignity reacting against humiliation, was like a breath of pure air, when compared with their futile endeavours. They saw in Stenka an embodiment of their liberated selves, and accordingly paid their tribute.

'After the experience with Messrs. B. & J., my contempt and pity for such Jews melted away like ice before the spring sun. I felt again humble in their presence. I began to see more in them than their often repulsive exteriors presented even to most sympathetic onlookers. Furthermore, I became more confident that the task we had set out to fulfill for ourselves, and for them, could and would be supported by the older generation: for I saw now, in a flash, that they were indispensable partners in our revolutionary aims. I had more than a notion that Stenka too, was aware of this, and drew from it the moral justification for his cruel tactics. The like of Messrs. B. & J. would have rebelled against such tactics, had they suspected that any artificial, diplomatic technique lay behind them. But in the case of Stenka they knew them to be genuine, instinctive and free of malice. No Jack, I certainly did not have it in me to follow Stenka's line, but I have been grateful to him ever since, for through him I came to see in the older generation not an antagonist but an ally. Yet, of course, this did not really simplify matters, for as you must know, it is a far more delicate business to deal with an ally than with an enemy. If you don't know this, ask any Cabinet-minister in London or Moscow.

'Looking at it from this point of view, you will be in a position to understand the dramatic sequence of events which gave us our first farm. And events which in their basically personal elements were similar, were to give us many more training opportunities. Indeed, I would go so far as to say that eventually, it was through such an interplay of elements that we obtained the means for our work in Palestine. Nevertheless, we had to be wary of our allies. They were not babes in the wood.'

Reuben then proceeded to tell me about the shock they received when their carts drew up, one fine spring morning at the farm. The land was certainly there; but houses and sheds were almost non-existent. The orchard was eaten up by parasites; and soon malaria made its appearance from bogs and marshes which were part of the estate. The boys and girls who came to take possession of the land were, of course, dispirited at first by what they saw. But the never-tiring Stenka very soon boosted up their morale by telling them to remember that any stretch of country they were likely to get in Palestine would be of the same nature, and it was just as well to gain experience by starting from virtually nothing. While Stenka was absent from the farm to scrounge tools, seeds, timber, food supplies and all the other necessities Reuben stayed to organise the biggest community he had yet had to manage. The conditions, as may be well imagined, were primitive enough to remind one of the stone age. But the work went on merrily, and with tremendous zest; and at last the community took shape and became capable of managing its own affairs.

Reuben could no longer find any excuse for refusing the call of a headquarters post. Moreover, he felt in his blood that he was ready for the task of leadership.

'So one morning', he continued, 'at the end of April, 1925, I mounted our old mare to make my way to the railway station. I had not been to bed that last night. The crowd, about a hundred merry boys and girls, celebrated their farewells with feasting, speeches, and folk-dances. When they went to bed, I remained with the new committee, discussing matters of economy and of the inner life of the community. When I mounted our old mare, the boys were already up and addressing their first blasphemous remarks to stubborn mules and cud-chewing bullocks. Girls' chirping voices came from the, as yet unwalled cowsheds, cajoling the patient beasts to part with their milk. I was happy and contented, and patting the neck of the mare I trotted off to take up new responsibilities.'

That was Reuben's parting shot, and just then the last post sounded and we turned in, expecting the usual alarm to send us hurrying to the shelters.

III

The Headquarters of the 'Young Watchers' was in Reuben's home town. So on arrival he made for his family's house, which he had left eighteen months before. His arrival came as a surprise – he had never mentioned it in the casual postcards he used to write home. When his sister opened the door she appeared to be uncertain whether the rustically dressed young man was her brother; Reuben helped her over the difficulty by hugging her robustly. Her cry assembled the rest of the family, with father in the background. A babel of excited voices greeted Reuben.

'Not to be recognised.'

'A veritable peasant indeed.'

'Double his size.'

'No flesh on him though – I bet he is hungry.'

'Don't crush my hand – you wood-chopper.'

'Shirt over his pants – a Russian mushik.'

It was father who put a stop to the hubbub. 'Now my son', he led Reuben to the table and signalled to big Sis to bring refreshments, 'I am glad you have come home. As far as I can see, work has done you no harm – but still, you had your experience and now I suppose you have come back to continue your studies.' Reuben, grave-faced and in a deep husky voice, still keeping his cracked fingers and horny hands out of sight deep in the pockets of his breeches, explained the position. He came he said, merely to pay his respects to the family, as his future duties would require his presence in the town. Father dropped the subject, dear to his heart quickly, when he grasped with consternation Reuben's hint of living out. 'What! to be in town and not live at home?' Father asked, and hurried on to explain that, of course, Reuben was now a man and nobody at home would interfere with his affairs. Reuben could not mean to shame the family, they all stormed in on him, by being in town and yet not living with them. Reuben – wisely enough – had no objection to living at home, provided that he was accepted on his own terms.

'Of course, of course', came the cries from all round him. Father had, it seemed to Reuben, some difficulty in keeping his eyes dry, and withdrew. Reuben's older brother, slapping him heartily on the back, revealed to him the secret that father's attitude had completely changed. He felt mighty proud of his youngest son, and his activities.

The old man himself, quite spontaneously, and for no reason Reuben could think of, was to leave a few years later, the comfort of his home and the joy of his first grandchild, to come and live on Reuben's settlement in Palestine. Reuben and his friends were only too glad to have him with them as he showed a profound understanding for their way of life. The old man would remark occasionally 'that a bit more Jewish religion would have done no harm to the community' – although – he added, 'what better religious service can there be than the redemption of the Holy Land?' His father, to whom Reuben became strongly attached, died in peace, while Reuben was anxiously waiting in a prison camp in Germany for a letter from him.

When Reuben arrived at headquarters to take up his duties, he was not yet nineteen years old, but what we know from his story so far makes it clear that he was not unprepared for the task. His plans and ambitions – his own words – kept surging in his veins when he was away from the movement; digging in the bog or making the rounds on the training farm. He wanted to do big things and carry out sweeping changes in the whole organisation of his beloved movement. Its growth was too slow for his liking, the organisation too stiff, and the type of youth embodied so far too exclusive and select. Reuben told me that he dreamed of a mass movement, encompassing every Jewish child in the country; he longed for an all-embracing, centrally directed organisation in place of the indifferently slumbering provincial tributaries; he saw in his vision, hundreds, yea thousands, of Workers on the training farms as hired labourers and as apprentices to craftsmen. Reuben dreamed of a united world movement of the Jewish pioneer youth, made up of all provincial clubs, developing in innumerable forms and varieties all over the world, and he had the ambition to be behind it all and to contribute towards its smooth running.

Before his time came to 'ascend' to Palestine, Reuben and his friends at the head of the movement, who shared his dreams and enthusiasm, toiled together for fifteen months; and when at the end of that time Reuben had to leave the country, he had the gratification of seeing most of his ambitions realised.

One utterance made by Reuben about himself during that period was of particular interest to me. He put it this way:

'The demarcation line between one's ideals and ambitions is, in fact, often blurred. Is it the ideal – a fixation of the mind – stirring one's ambition – an emotional desire – or is it the other way round? One thing is certain that the man of ideals is normally subject to a tense emotional state driving him to action. And as the emotional state is doubtless a primary attribute of our physical make-up, it may well be that the ambitions stirring in our nerve systems give rise to the purposefulness of our consciousness, which is later crystallized into ideals. That may also explain why ambitions and idealism are amoral as such – the moral valuation comes in later when we apply the social criterion in the sense of *cui bono*.

'However that may be', he enlarged, 'I believe that the pull-and-push forces emanating from the ambitions and idealism of individuals or groups, affecting society as a whole, have been in the past strong incentives for progress, or more correctly for changes. The stagnation of our present civilization for instance, appears to me not only the result of our blind surrender to the economic profit principle; but above all the outcome of the prevailing mediocrity in ambition and idealism. The glorification of the past and of tradition, which is the underlying principle of all conservative societies, leaves not much room for ambition and idealism. As I see it, the handkering after past glories has, of its very nature, little in common with idealism, for such leanings are the very opposite of idealism and should properly be classed as the last flicker of dying ambitions.'

'What, when you come to think of it, do we at present ask of the individual? By "we" I mean those institutions representing the demand, or the pull, such as church, state, parties and philosophies. To answer their demands no individual need strain his intellectual or moral standards. His purse, and in its absence, his muscles would normally suffice to provide the balance. On the contrary, the more shallow, commonplace, unthinking and unambitious one is, the easier it is for one to conform to the demands imposed on one by society to-day.

'What am I after – you ask? Well, I would wish to see the intellectual and moral demands really forming a part of our lives. Indeed to such an extent as would appear to us to be on an Utopian level. Have not individuals, classes and whole civilizations attained heights which have been declared impossible and fantastic by their contemporaries? Do we know how far we can go in our demand – what is "too much"? We can only know what is too little, because then the ideal is on the same level as the actuality, and inertia is the result. That is the state in which our civilization stood, prior to the present war. That is – I come at last back to my topic – where as a matter of fact my movement found the ideals and ambitions of Jewry – on a dead level with the actual reality. You will find it – I am afraid – in your own country and among all people who cling to our present social order.

'And – wait a moment! – when we enforce the demands of intellect and character on our Jewish youth to what many sober brains call derisively an Utopian pitch – have we failed? Not a bit. Of course we shall never achieve our ideals, for a living movement takes care to keep its ideals well beyond and in advance of easy achievement.'

'Well, Reuben, that is all right as long as you deal with the few and the select', I put in, 'but your method could scarcely be applied to broad masses of people, or mass movements. If you raise your ideals above the level of the masses, you will find yourself in complete isolation on some forlorn height, with no say in the affairs of the world.'

'Not a bit of it,' reiterated Reuben, 'in fact you would be hard put to it to show me a movement – in the political, social, or religious field – which grew eventually into a mass movement, without having aspired from the outset to what contemporaries have classed as Utopian ideals or ambitions? My contention applies to all religions and the modern social and political movements – they all pitched their ideals and ambition far above an attainable level. As a matter of fact, the first thing I encountered when I put forward my ambitious programme was the question of quality and quantity. I believe that in our case we have demonstrated generally and in particular to the political parties which vigorously contested our philosophy or method, that quality and

quantity are not mutually exclusive. We became the mass movement in the Jewish world thanks to the "Utopian" demands we
made on Jewish youth. Such movements, which in the name of
the masses and in order to gain their support have maintained
their demands on the commonplace level (which meant no
particular effort on the part of the individual) have remained
barren, poor and sterile and have indeed gained no mass
following. Our movement has striven for, and reached the masses
– ten thousand in Rumania, and hundreds of thousands all over
the Jewish world. And mark you, we make no compromise, there
is no bargaining with our demand; away from shops and universities to hard manual labour; away from a social order of profit
and selfishness, to a society based on co-operation; and away from
a medley of languages to one unifying national language –
Hebrew; a readiness to emigrate to Palestine; legally if possible;
if not, by smuggling ourselves across borders and seas; away from
atavistic religious fatalism to constructive positive action; out of
the parochial conventicle to a world solidarity of Jewish pioneer
youth; against the tribal-father authority of the old generation,
and for the self-leadership of youth, and so on to innumerable
cataclysmic uprootings from old ways of life. These were some of
our demands – by no means elementary for my generation.

'You may think me a braggart, Jack, well go and look for yourself, the evidence is there writ large, on our work in Palestine,
complete with its own trade mark: "made by the Jewish youth".
Quality and quantity? If you have the one you will get the other,
because, with the many come also the select of the people.'

That effort had completely exhausted Reuben for a while, and
I was free to work out for myself the patch-work quilt of Jewish
life, on which his movement burst with such relentless force. I
learned that about a million Jews lived in his part of the Balkans –
split up into four distinct cultural spheres. One section had been
brought up in Russian schools, and on Russian culture, before
having had the Rumanian tongue and way of life thrust upon it.
Another section had the German tongue and Austrian civilization, as its background; another community had had the Hungarian language and traditions; and the fourth had belonged to
the old Rumanian circle, with Rumanian as their language and
French thought and letters for their cultured life. Each of these
fragments of Jewry, brought together under the same oppressive
political roof, had acquired in the past different usages, manners

and philosophies. The Bessarabians had never seen a mountain peak; the people of Bukovina had never heard of Nihilism and bomb throwers; the Transylvanians never touched anything which was not kosher; and the Old Rumanians never bathed in cold water – unless it were perfumed.'

'And there is something else, Jack, for your album', broke in Reuben to help in my effort to get my bearings in that jungle. 'While all the Gentiles who had been united under the Rumanian crown by victoriously ignorant diplomats had nothing in common between them, all the Jewish communities, hailing from similarly divergent spheres as the Gentiles, had yet a few fundamental ties, which "nilly-willy" marked them as one whole. You will say, of course, religion. I do not deny that the Jewish religion was a powerful unifying force, but there were also considerable numbers for whom religion had very little meaning. But even with them religion had left a strong residue of Hebrew and biblical lore, which gave them a common denominator. What in fact was most pronounced was their national and racial unity.

'When the Jews became hard-pressed and penalized by the official anti-semitic policy, they reacted, not as a religious, but as a national unit, exactly as Ukrainians, Poles, or Germans, would have done. How did that come about, you ask? All text-books of *rerum politicarum* tell how such characteristics have not been present in the case of Jewish communities here or there in any part of the world. It follows then that the Jews could not be classed as a nation! Not only Gentile political scholars, but also large groups of Jews – mostly of the wealthy classes have thought and still think the same about it. They believe that their position would improve if they classed themselves as members of the majority nations with which they became associated. Therefore, when you ask them – Russian Jews? No, Russians! German Jews? No, Germans with an appendix of mosaic religion. English Jews? Oh, no. Englishmen. That experiment ended in failure long before Hitler, but it was reserved for a disaster of unprecedented proportions to drive it home to the consciousness of Jews and non-Jews alike. One can and may deceive oneself and one's neighbour for a while but eventually it is certain to come to light; most probably when and where it is least expected. One has frequently heard of cases where ill-concealed derision behind the back of an assimilated Jew opened a searing wound in his heart; he became disillusioned and bitter and craved for revenge.

'I notice from the grimace on your face that you fail to see the consequences of the frustrated assimilation effort. Well, think for yourself. There have been no outbreaks against religions in our day – have there? The violent revival of anti-Semitism, is not synonomous with an anti-Jewish religious feeling of the mediæval pattern, no, not even in Germany! It is an anti-Jewish sentiment – the term semitic cloaks the issue – fed by an elementary antipathy against an alien race and nation, and not against an alien religion. And who in Christendom would call the Mosaic religion an alien religion – anyway? Even a Delitzsch, writing with truly talmudistic skill failed to rescue Christianity from its Judaistic parent. Most of the Gentiles, and some of the Jews, are reluctant to acknowledge the positive evidence we offer, proving that the Jews are a nation primarily and foremost, but can they truthfully support the negative evidence of their own making? Are then, the text-books wrong? Their definition of a nation's characteristics lacks one word. They should say that the characteristics of a *normal* nation are such and such; it is the abnormality of the Jewish national existence, which is the basis of all the antisemitic or anti-Jewish sentiments and outbreaks.

'You will remember the case of Jewry in Rumania – where the four sections of Jewry united swiftly, while the different Gentile communities, all Christian, failed to do so – this can only be ascribed to the fact that the Jews felt as one nation, whereas the Christians represented several different nationalities. That is the only reason I can think of, why all the Jews in the world act and feel like a national unit, disabled as it is by the loss of its national territorial concentration. Whether the Jews themselves wish for or recognise this, is immaterial.

'To come to smaller things – in that intrinsic, national, collective feeling, you will find the other reason why my work in the movement grew and expanded swiftly, and made in the course of one year, out of all the small parochial bodies, one solidly united movement. All our youngsters behind the Russian, German or Rumanian façade were of course, Jews first and last and they knew it. What they did not perceive at first, and had to be told and taught was that it was useless and humiliating to masquerade as something else. A load was taken off them by our educational work, and our youth came to know true emancipation for the first time in their lives – for we brought them emancipation both from innocent illusion and deliberate falsehood.'

I believe that what, according to Reuben's account, had happened in one country, happened all over Europe and America, where large sections of Jewry gave up attempting to be individually assimilated, and began to fight for recognition of their claims as a nation, as well as for equal civilian rights, Reuben's point was elucidated for me by a passage I came across in a book by Professor Toynbee. It reads:

'. . . thus in the Zionist view the emancipation and assimilation of the Jew as an individual, is a wrong method of pursuing a right aim. If they (the Jews) are to succeed in becoming "like all the nations", they must seek assimilation on a national, and not an individual basis. Instead of trying to assimilate individual Jews to individual Englishmen or Frenchmen, they must try to assimilate Jewry itself to England or France. Jewry must become a nation in effective possession of a national home, and this on the grounds from which the historic roots of Judaism have sprung.'

When I showed the quotation to Reuben he could not say enough to praise and exalt the terseness of Professor Toynbee's statement. It was however, one thing to clarify the idea, and quite another to equip the Jewish youth with adequate weapons for its materialisation. The Zionists even had they been given unlimited immigration facilities would have, so I understood, refused to contemplate the transfer of the Jewish youth to Palestine in their 'exilic shape'. Reuben's ideas required for their realisation a new social type of man; a retempering of character and intellect, and a ruthless physical metamorphosis. For such revolutionary changes in the life of the individual he and his friends had only such educational means at their disposal, as a voluntary youth movement under its own leadership had been able to create. In such a movement they toiled for fifteen months under a never relaxing strain. They had, of course, little money with which to work; all journeys, covering the country from end to end had to be made in cattle trucks (Balkan 4th class), on carts, sleighs and any other chance conveyance. Great quantities of educational instruction manuals, schemes for vacational camps, courses for instructors and guides for all age-groups had to be composed and distributed. At the same time, they had to shield themselves against ever-recurring sabotage by reactionary Jewish authorities, as well as by the state authorities. Reuben was merely a guest at his home during that time. Five days out of seven he was on tours in the provinces, in camps or instructing new leaders assembled in seminaries during vacations.

The migration aim in their ideology compelled them to keep a look-out for every spark of new talent which might stand out from among the hundreds of new recruits. The large-scale growth of the movement would not be allowed to debase its coinage. To maintain a high standard of leadership, more and more talent and sterling character had to be uncovered, encouraged, and woven into the pattern of the organisation.

'The problem of finding leaders and instructors became acute', explained Reuben, 'as soon as we laid the foundation of our first immigration community, which was to go to Palestine in a body, to start the building of a new collective settlement. Hitherto, our "Workers" who had finished their manual training, passed the severe tests and been admitted for immigration – sailed singly or in small groups. Once in Palestine, they joined already established settlements, or founded new collective groups in conjunction with pioneers of our brother movements of other countries. With the growth of the movement and of our productivization training, we were in a position to found our own settlement, to which we were all eagerly looking forward. Apart from the merit in itself we believed it also to be of great educational and moral value for the movement. Our aim was to create loyalty and attachment to the abstract idea of "working Palestine"; an infinitely more difficult task than the development and cultivation of such sentiments for our own settlement of the "mother movement."

'With the "ascent" of the first party to Palestine, a good many of our active leaders went, and new people had to be introduced to take their place. The solution was found in due course by the despatch of missions from our settlements in Palestine to the movement in the Diaspora. That system had the additional effect of making experience acquired in the real life in Palestine available to the movement at large. It also brought our educational work into direct contact with the life of the collective working communities – which embodied the ethical and educational ideals of the movement.'

Reuben, detained by a decision of headquarters, to introduce and guide the new staff taking over the duties of their predecessors, did not go to Palestine with the first group. For the next few months he spent most of his time at headquarters, directing the work of the new regional leaders. Thanks to its growth and strength, the movement, imperceptibly at first, became a potent factor in the life of organised Jewry. Neither friend nor foe among the representative bodies of Jewry was now in a position to ignore Reuben's organisation. Without the co-operation of the 'Young Watcher' no large-scale activity could be undertaken, nor would any activity directed against the interests of Zionism cut any ice if the movement stood up against it. Both the quality and the size of the ever-growing movement gave its leaders an important standing in the life of Jewry, but on the other hand it also presented them with a new problem. Should a youth movement get entangled with the party politics of the adult, take sides, send its representatives to public bodies; or what form, if any, should the participation of the movement in public affairs take?

It was a case of *noblesse oblige.*

'There was no dodging the issue', Reuben remarked. 'With the rejection of Baruch's philosophy the movement declared itself positively and actively for the Zionist renaissance, which, applied to the Jewish youth was tantamount to a personal social revolution of the individual. Consequently, we could not remain indifferent to the way the affairs of Jewry in the Diaspora were to be directed. Naturally enough our sympathies were with the Zionist-Socialist trend – but from the point of view of the young, there was little difference in character, disinterestedness and public morals between the different groups. Ethical kinship counted with us innocents still more than ideological relations. To send our delegates to the representative bodies of the adult, meant invariably to get entangled in party intrigue – which is, I am afraid, quite unavoidable in political life – and to have in due course the whole mess of party tactics dragged into the movement. We decided – and I think it was, and still remains the wisest course for every movement of youth possessed of sincere educational ambitions – not to send our representatives there. We made our views on this matter of principle known through our magazine, in memoranda, but chiefly in private talks and, when necessary, brought pressure to bear on the Jewish authorities to bring them into line with our views. We declined, in an "uppish" way I confess, all formal participation in, and responsibility for, the policy of representative bodies. I believe that our attitude kept the movement clean and out of that danger – hovering over every type of youth movement – of degenerating into a mere tool in the hands of politicians.

'On the other hand much was done for the political education

of our youth which took the form of instruction in the fundamental social sciences such as economy, history, sociology, and
theories of socialism and liberalism. They were taught that active
politics were the privilege and duty of the adult, which meant in
our case that political life would begin with immigration and
settlement in Palestine. Needless to say our attitude failed to
please the politicians of all parties, who raged against our "aristo-
cratic isolationism" from "Gegenwartspolitik". They resented
above all that such fruitful territory was excluded from the influence of their propaganda. We remained stubbornly independent
of all parties, yet not indeterminate in our political philsophy and
views.'

Reuben's activity in the Balkans was cut short by the benign
interference of the Rumanian government. A few months previously he had been ordered to present himself for conscription,
to a medical army board. He was found fit for the cavalry. When
he eventually received the order to join the army he decided to
bolt.

To waste two years of his life in a Balkan conscript army never
entered his mind. The obvious alternative was to make straight
for Palestine – but the British government in London, and the
Palestine administration suffered just then one of their recurring
fits of appeasement. There was some unemployment in Palestine,
to be sure, due almost entirely to the pricking of the tobacco
bubble. By a curious whim of nature a farmer managed to produce
a crop of high grade tobacco – with no further ado whole crowds
began to join in the fun; everybody – particularly of the Polish
middle-class immigrants – began planting tobacco. The inevitable
happened – instead of tobacco, weeds and thorns were harvested.
Considerable capital investments were irretrievably lost, and what
was doubtless a severe blow to a certain class of new immigrants
was swiftly construed by the Arab Mufti – later of Axis fame –
into a great economic calamity for the whole country. The docile
Palestine government taking the same view promptly put a stop
to immigration, which precipitated the crisis longed for by the
Mufti and certain Government circles in Jerusalem. As a result
there was no immigration certificate for Reuben, and he had to
leave the country forthwith, otherwise his good passport would
have lost its validity.

'I decided to go to Berlin', Reuben told me on one occasion.
'Why Berlin?' 'Well, I had been on several previous occasions to

other capitals of Eastern and Central Europe, and there was little in them to attract me. I knew that it would take me some time to find my way to Palestine, and thought the enforced period of delay would provide me with an excellent opportunity for study. After three years of work for others, of organising, speaking, and instructing, I felt dry and hollow. In truth my reserves were exhausted and there was nothing left in me upon which to draw. I badly needed a re-charging of the batteries, before setting out on the greatest adventure of all! – Palestine. Berlin offered good and cheap opportunities for study; I had some friends and well-wishers there, and in the year 1926 it was still a centre of much political, economic and artistic thought and initiative. I hoped to earn my living by teaching Hebrew and other related subjects to the Jewish youth in Berlin; as I refused to be kept by father's money.

'The parting from my friends, and they were legion by the end of my service years, was not as easy as I had imagined. The ties which bound me to the movement and to outside friends, appeared much stronger than I had believed them to be. It had to be done, however, and when I boarded the train in the middle of a winter night I had some difficulty in wrenching myself, not only from friends, but also from my own family, who had grown much attached to my work and interests. They had, to all appearances, travelled a very long way since the days when I had had to run away from home to be free to follow my chosen path.

'When the train moved out of the station, I felt my heart overflowing with gratitude and thanksgiving for all the experiences the world of my youth had so generously bestowed on me. My thanks went impartially and sincerely to everybody and everything, to mountain and stream, to my family and friends, to sympathiser and antagonist, but above all to the Jewish youth whom I followed, and who followed me. As the train swept me across borders and countries I could scarcely believe in the reality of it all. The years of my youth rolled past in review as I leaned in the corner of my third-class compartment, as if I were looking at a film picture representing an alien world. Slowly my mind turned to dreams of the future which steadily replaced the reminiscences of the past. Although full of events, I knew that so far it had been mere play and fun. The test lay ahead. Thank heaven for the blessing conferred on a young man of twenty, which moves him not to dwell on past achievements, but to turn his gaze upon the strife and conquest of the future. The field of conquest in my case', concluded Reuben, 'appeared to be plainly mapped out for me. It was to conquer weak bodies and hereditary fickle minds for the task imposed on them. For untold generations, both the bodies and minds of young Jews had not been born or bred for such conquest. And what if we were to fail?'

With that final question Reuben turned to me for an answer. But I understood that the question, 'And what if we were to fail?' opened for the like of Reuben, such degrading vistas of humiliation as to be unthinkable. The doubt which the question expressed was not to be found in the rectitude or practicability of the ideal, but in the fitness of the vessel to hold such strong and precious substance.

CHAPTER FOUR

ALIYAH

I

A MONG the outstanding experiences of my P.O.W. life, I will always rank the acquaintance with Donald MacDuff and his 'colonial' crowd.

Donald himself was not a colonial, but he had been in many parts of the Commonwealth and colonies. He declared himself in love with the Empire, and particularly with Rhodesian Africa. Donald was not averse to the nickname of 'Don Africanus', bestowed on him by his fellow-prisoners on account of his scheme for making the Rhodesias and 'anything which lies round them' the administrative and strategic metropolis of the future Government of the Commonwealth. For that purpose he had in mind to settle in Rhodesia say 8-10 million Britons from the British Isles. Such an exotic idea might induce you to consider Donald a crank enthusiast for hare-brained schemes – a mild and not infrequent example of the aberration of British genius – thrown out, it would appear, for the purpose of exasperating scholars of the 'British character'.

Donald MacDuff, swathed coquettishly in a quilt, the owner of a finely chiselled, intellectual face, was certainly not the possessor of an aberration, and that explains the hold he had on most of us. I wish and expect to hear him one day expounding his views from the rostrum of Parliament. Donald was the first Socialist I had met who had no difficulty – either of a conscientious or ideological nature – in adhering to the imperialistic idea, although, to be fair, his conception of it was quite different from what is normally presented and argued about in our political controversies.

To begin with I had little or no interest at all in the matter. All questions appertaining to inter-Dominion relations, India, and similar familiar colonial troubles, I believed to be quite safe in the hands of experts, and cared for by professional politicians. I took pride in the quiet and self-confident solidarity of the British peoples – of England and the Dominions, and as to India and the colonies, well – I believed that we were making the best of a bad job. The colonial problem I held to be in the nature of obligations and responsibilities which could not be discarded, although the adventurous spirit of my ancestors who have saddled my generation with such a glorious inheritance, did not win my sympathies. After all even great states like America and Russia – I reasoned to myself – managed to get their cocoa and rubber without implanting the 'white man's burden' principle on a multitude of happy-go-lucky native races. I did not even bother to enquire whether such reasoning was based on facts, or more likely on some sort of pious American or Russian propaganda.

But not so Donald. His keen intellect, of a quaint texture composed of a velvety poetical softness and a brittle political harshness, dissolved the complicated mystery of Empire, natives, and emigration, into a well ordered pattern. Already, in his first challenging lecture on the subject, he succeeded in nailing his ideas to the door-post of my consciousness.

'We are trifling with a great inheritance', Donald shot at us in crisp sentences, not omitting to roll his R's like thunder. 'That may sound like sentimental trash to those who have neither sense nor sentiment. Well, where do we stand logically and materially? (May the Lord forgive the creator of that word!) We are the living witnesses of the relentless annihilation process of all that is petty and narrow, in the political and economic life of the world. Europe, the balance of power in Europe, the wars and miseries of Europe, the world domineering ambitions of that Asiatic promontory – breathe their last. For better or for worse – I believe it to be for the better – the future belongs to the big aggregates of international and economic Unions. Russia – a hundred races and more in one gigantic economic and political union; the U.S.A., where fifty nationalities have built, and are still engaged in building a new world; the gigantic, as yet politically and economically feeble, masses of China – where, I ask, will a little Englishman stand in such a Universe? Is it not fantastic to think, that we in Britain taught the world the lesson of political and economic union between four nations (not yet consolidated because of Eire) and we, the British peoples, have planted the seed for the growth of new nations. America and our Dominions began their careers with British stock, but now they are consolidated as new and complex national and political units. It was emigration on account of religious persecution, adventurous greed, and great political wisdom which has built it that way. Remember the Pilgrim

Fathers – as the Americans call the early British immigrants proudly. Their movement began in England, with money subscribed *"for the glory of Christ and the advancement of the beaver trade',* and yet those who sailed with the 'Mayflower' – three and a half centuries ago – laid it down as their aim:

'to covenant and combine themselves together into a civil body politic.'

So they knew what they were after – and the same applies to others who followed their lead to other quarters of the globe. The pilgrim's progress has not yet exhausted itself, as many dullards think. Millions of Britons will and must build a new Metropolis for the Commonwealth – I suggest it should be built in Rhodesia.'

Donald proceeded to describe in glowing terms the strategic and economic advantages of such a centre, as against London 'a stone's throw from a vicious continent, lying as it does on the outskirts of the Commonwealth'. Donald argued that a new metropolis for the Commonwealth should be founded in order to meet the all-too justifiable prejudices to Whitehall and Downing Street of the one-time colonies. But Africa as the economic strategic centre of the Commonwealth would obviously be rejected by our present-day unimaginative generation, and as Donald would not like to have the main issue spoilt by his Rhodesian vision, he was ready to waive that point for the time being in order to progress with the task of re-organisation.

When Donald came to deal with inter-Empire relations, he was acclaimed enthusiastically by the Dominion and colonial crowd – who, except for the two Rhodesians, had kept ominous silence during the first part of the talk.

'Migration – colonisation – nation and state building – are the milestones of British growth. It is the sound, natural, and I think, never-ending story, spun by man's urge to settle and to raise his material and spiritual standards. The last three decades in our history, provide the anti-climax of constructive thought and deeds. The dole, Piccadilly Circus, bankrupt estates, distressed areas, slums and night-clubs, have smothered the manly adventure of migration. Ask your friends from the Dominions. They got their capital in pre-war times with a finer grace, and moreover with a lower rate of interest, from Wall Street than from the City; our industry did not think it worth while to trouble about the special requirements of our Dominions and Colonies – although American firms found it profitable. And now, what about your own

narrow-mindedness, you people of the Dominions (this time rue-
ful silence from the Dominion crowd and "hear, hear" from the
"little Englishmen"). The people and Governments of the
Dominions, what views or prejudices did you hold on immigration? You scorned the American experiment, and I say – blessed
be America. By breaking away from us she escaped stagnation,
and threw off parochial blinkers. In taking such a leap in the dark,
old and new immigrants combined in the creation of a new
world. It is the line which our Commonwealth must take now. As
I see it, the building and development of the Commonwealth has
just passed the experimental stage, for the next phase we want
greater vision and up-to-date organisation, immigration programmes for British and kindred nationalities, catering for
millions of people, an all-Empire economic board, the establishment of stable international relations between the Commonwealth
and the other big Unions of States, all these demand urgently the
creation of a democratic Commonwealth Government, composed
and directed by the legislative assemblies of England and the
Dominions until such time as an all-Commonwealth legislature
might be ready to adopt a new and adequate constitution for the
body-politic of the British domains.'

Here, Donald reached a point at which only few were able or
willing to follow him. For he insisted that we were facing the
inescapable alternatives of either converting the Empire by successive and gradual measures into a multi-national Commonwealth, or of seeing it reduced to a purely British, and very much
restricted organisation. Donald envisaged the inclusion of India,
the Arab Federation, a Jewish-Palestine state, and many of the
African possessions as members of the Commonwealth, though
not necessarily on the Dominion basis. But he also saw imperative
reasons for the opening of the Commonwealth to many Western
European nations, such as Belgians, Dutch and Norwegians, in
order to give stability and security to all concerned. No wonder
that only few showed themselves capable of breathing this rarified
air of dreamland. Donald on the other hand, his inner fire well
under control, thought he was expounding mere platitudes, and
that his audience was lulled into stupor by the vision of ancient
Eldorados, swallowed up as they were by the march of ruthless
evolutionary events.

Donald MacDuff – Highlander, poet, teacher and budding
politician – felt strongly about the rights of small nations, as

might be expected of a staunch Scot. With the same fervour with which he advocated the great political and economic Unions, he also stood up for the liberty – cultural, educational, national – of all nations and tribes, large or small. He believed that Soviet Russia had found the right answer to the problem of adjusting the legitimate claims of the national individuality with the economic and political necessities of our time, which call for the maintenance of International Unions.

'The granting of National autonomy in cultural and educational spheres, and of regional executive powers, under the ægis of central planning and legislative bodies – would satisfy the reasonable demands of every nation – Scots included. The prosperity of a nation can only be secured by its being a member of a big and powerful aggregate of nations, as provided by a Union or a Commonwealth." These are mere clumsily resuscitated extracts from McDuff's inexhaustible well of ideas. It was hopeless to argue with him, because any such attempt only gave rise to a new crop of thought-adventures. Who can blame me for getting myself immersed, for a time at any rate – all prison life consists of stretches of time denoted by the length of a certain experience – in the hundred and one questions relating to Dominions, Commonwealth, immigration, planning schemes and so on.

I did not guess then how useful my new Empire education under MacDuff would be to me in comprehending Reuben's story, which otherwise I should have found almost incomprehensible and consequently should not have been able to tell here.

I wanted first to reassure myself as to the views of our friends from the Dominions. There could, I knew, be no doubt as to their sentiments, although they showed themselves extremely wary in endorsing Donald's ideas. It took me some time to realise, and then it came as a shock to me – that they, the Dominion people, so wholeheartedly British in outlook, culture, and sentimental ties, had nevertheless grown up to manhood as independent nationals. We here, on our Isles, still speak of Scottish and English, but these descendants of Scottish and English spoke of themselves as Canadians, Australians and South Africans. And indeed, close observation made it manifest, that although decidedly of British stock, the different climes and countries have moulded a new national type, proudly conscious of its own characteristics in language, customs and social life. As such our

Dominion friends showed a somewhat hesitant reaction to the idea of cementing the existing sentimental and racial links by a new central organisation of the Commonwealth as a whole. We, of the motherland, on the other hand, had less apprehensions in following MacDuff's call than our friends in the Dominions. That aspect – which never occurred to me before – made me even more eager to pursue the subject. Can we be sure – I asked myself and my friends – that racial and sentimental links would stand the test should material interests or national security point another way? Many of my friends reading the anxious query from words unspoken made light of it. Others, and the undaunted MacDuff among them, had, what appeared to them, a simple answer at hand: 'Union with the United States'. MacDuff had a name ready for the most gigantic political and economic Union of all times – the A.A.F.S. The Anglo-American Federated States. (The British Commonwealth and the U.S.A.). 'The Dominions', he said, 'considered it as their rightful and imposed task to provide the bridge over which the re-union of the English-speaking world would eventually cross. It would be easier for them to accept the obligations resulting from a Union of Atlantic and Pacific spheres, than to dissociate themselves from the new world, by an even more absolute association with the old. Sentiment, interest and security all play their part in winning over the mature minds of the Dominions for such an orientation. Why not attempt it?' Since such a daring economic and political edifice could not be constructed, nay, scarcely even begun, by one generation – why not then lay the first brick by converting the war-time alliance into the first, embryonic stage of the future Union?'

Undaunted MacDuff, he would never surrender and give himself beaten. But as for me, having been dragged into that whirlpool quite accidentally, the waters became too deep to negotiate.

After MacDuff's hurricane Reuben appeared to me as a sure haven in which to shelter. He had his contacts with MacDuff, and knew about his schemes long before I heard of them. I could see them both in full agreement – if not on the actual subject, at least in principle. I do not know what prompted me to tread on Reuben's most sensitive corn, I should have known that anything connected with migration and related subjects, would provoke him intensely. And so it did – though I am ashamed to admit that I enjoyed his subsequent wrath enormously.

'Are you, Reuben, also among the New Imperialists?' I asked

him banteringly on a sunny winter morning.

'Don't you worry about that, Mr. Wiseacre', he looked daggers at me. 'At present, your Government keeps us at arm's length, not only excluding us from your own Commonwealth, but also from the little strip of land which is ours by right and by necessity. I don't mind telling you what I think about MacDuff's line of thought. But I shall look at it as your Government wants me to look at it, as an outsider. Furthermore, I look on the question from the point of view of the client – the immigrant – "And remember that thou wast a servant in Egypt" is still a deeply felt reality with me. Were everyone to remember it as I do, mankind could have been saved from many miseries. What people was not at some time or other of its history subjugated by alien races?'

'What has that to do with our imperial problems, or with Mac-Duff's ideas, for that matter?' I asked, rather annoyed.

'I am sorry, Jack, but I do think that the immigration problem is the crux of the whole question. I may be wrong, but I have a hunch that the large majority of the peoples in the Dominions have forgotten that they themselves were immigrants, or at least their immediate descendants. Moreover, they have almost persuaded themselves to believe, and they expect the whole world to take their word for it, that having arrived in the country first they now have a stronger claim to it than the immigrants who knock in vain at the door. There is also too much self-conceit in rating the older migration waves as qualitatively higher than the contemporary ones. The cry went out, that the new immigration was responsible for the lowering of the standard of living, and for the cyclic economic depressions. "The World" rightly or wrongly got the impression that the Dominions stood for anti-immigration. Within the half century in which the U.S.A. had absorbed sixty million immigrants from England and from the continent, the Dominions had indeed increased their population, but at what rate, and how timidly! The British Commonwealth came to be regarded by Continentals and Americans alike as being the epitome of grasping selfishness, keeping as they were huge spaces sealed up, and out of reach of those who, squeezed by economic religions and national persecution, were clamouring for somewhere to settle in peace.'

'But Reuben', I did not get farther than that.

Reuben read my objection instantly, for he proceeded. 'Yes, I agree that such criticism was not always fair, and only seldom disinterested. But that is irrelevant. What really matters is that the British Commonwealth having acted as the pioneers of colonization, having had the lion's-share in the development of primeval worlds – has failed to follow up the heroic drive of the pioneers, by large scale immigration of British and other stock. We see it now that the accumulation of wealth by trade and through bills of exchange is not as lasting and faithful an asset as firmly-planted and well-amalgamated humanity. The upward trend of the accruing wealth made you blind to the poignant symptoms of futility and stagnation in the Commonwealth, to which the halt in immigration and colonization in your domains had contributed a fair share.'

'What you say, Reuben, may be correct or not; there is no denying the fact that the British people felt no urge to emigrate, and consequently the Dominions, in order to preserve their national-cultural character, were reluctant to admit non-British immigration – which, if encouraged, might have changed radically the make-up of the newly-formed nations of the Commonwealth. No Government regulations could make people emigrate from England when they did not wish to do so.'

'Exactly. Conditions have certainly changed since the days of Laud and Stuart absolutism. The days have passed – I believe forever – when adventurous spirits are rewarded with treasure and spoil. You cannot have it both ways, you know. If the British peoples are content on their islands, and have no use for further emigration, and if the immigration of even great men and their families threatens the purity of character of the Dominion nations – then there is no alternative but that Canberra and Ottawa should continue a stark-sterile anti-immigration policy. As none of the Dominions appear to be inclined to improve on the pre-war immigration policy – some way out of the dilemma must be suggested.'

'Well at last we are on firm ground. Everybody appears now to be agreed – Dominions and Homeland – that the growth and development of the Commonwealth by immigration and settlement should be resumed again, with vigour. Where do we go from there?'

'You are pushing me relentlessly into the abyss, Jack. You seem to be intent on stamping me, in the eyes of your readers, as a meddlesome busybody, who knows of other men's business though scarcely of his own. Under the circumstances, I may as well go the "whole hog". I suggest then, the opening to British youth of new channels of adventure romance and hard work; when I say youth, I mean the youth of all classes of the population, and not of the unemployed or distressed only. Even though the prospects of stock-brokers, city clerks and of colonial officials promise to be in the future highly adventurous, and yet not too strenuous! I believe, nevertheless, that what the Dominions have to offer might appeal more strongly to the vigorous and idealistic section of British youth, provided it is made known through your educational and social systems. I believe that MacDuff, for instance – and he should not be regarded as a mere exotic specimen of the Scottish Highlands – and men and women of his mettle could start such a movement among British youth.'

'Granting that MacDuff's ideals catch fire among our youth, and as a result a steady, well-organised and carefully-planned immigration stream does materialise, it would still leave open the question of non-British immigration. I feel that we ought to do something constructive to gather the continental overflow into our Dominions, particularly when one considers that British emigration alone would certainly not satisfy the demand. The Australian Government, for instance, appears to work on immigration schemes which envisage increasing the population of the country by about fifteen millions. Other dominions contemplate similar relatively gigantic schemes. It is obvious that in such a case the bulk of the immigrants must come from the Continent. Don't misunderstand me, Reuben, I am very much in favour of it, but I am anxious to see the schemes for England and the Continent adjusted and interwoven, so as to make an organic whole.'

'I entirely agree with you,' he replied, 'the planning and execution of such schemes should not be too difficult, provided that the initiative is not left with the shipping companies, or with any other profit-making concerns. I know enough of Continental conditions to foresee the post-war conditions of Central and Western Europe. One might expect a strong urge, and a ready willingness among the youth, to get away from a Europe which is persistently devouring its own offspring even before they come to maturity. A Commonwealth Immigration Board would be in a position to organise such willingness into the framework of an adequate educational organisation. It would then be in a position to ensure for the migrating youth adequate training facilities and schooling, in order to acquire the English language, and a general knowledge of the social and cultural conditions prevailing in their future homes. You may find in such an undertaking the pre-requisite of more intimate contacts between British and Contin-ental youth, pursuing the same object. Such unity of purpose, and of management, might also answer many of your anxious questions as to whether mixed settlements of British and non-British youth should not be developed as against the traditional way of jealously separated national communities. Judging by our experiences in Palestine, such mixed training and settlement centres might well be the easiest and speediest device for a smooth and painless acclimatisation in the new environment.'

'I doubt it very much,' I replied, 'in fact, I am sure that large-scale migrations have never been conducted on strictly scientific lines. Your suggestion, notwithstanding, might prove a valuable contribution to the solution of the problem. But, after all, immi-gration is primarily not a question of organisation or of educa-tional propaganda. There must be a stimulus or a natural urge for it, and I still doubt whether our youth feels anything like it or could be made to feel it by means of ideological appeals. It is possible that perhaps the present war may have created new and live contacts among the peoples of the Commonwealth, thus lending a fresh impetus for migration.'

'I certainly envy the predicament in which you seem to find yourself. My trouble is of quite a different nature. You have vast spaces calling for settlers and builders, and yet you doubt whether immigrants would be forthcoming – for my people the problem is exactly reversed. I know what that means, as not so long ago I personally was a potential immigrant with all the urges required by the text-books – and yet, I could scarcely find an entry into the country which even official British and international declarations pronounced "my national home".'

'Of course! I had almost forgotten that when I last heard from you, you were sitting in a railway coach on the way to Berlin. We must get on with our story, you know . . . the war is drawing to a close . . . and how am I going to track you down once we are outside the barbed wire?'

I wrote down the conversation with Reuben on MacDuff's ideas verbatim, because thanks to it I stumbled on Reuben's migration story. I had not been prepared for it – for instead of an account of a journey to Palestine which I expected to hear – Reuben unfolded a stirring tale of Jewish migrations in which his own adventure appeared in his own words 'as a mere speck of dust, only observed when passing through a cone of light'. As the story developed, it became increasingly difficult to keep Reuben's personal experiences apart from the experience of his race. They grew into one occasionally pathetic cry of a people which had not been allowed to settle in a place for more than a short historical hour, then to be kicked or lured into movement again. I actually started the ball rolling myself by a harmless suggestion as to the effect a restoration of democracy might have on the solution of the Jewish question. The Continent would then naturally restore the Jews to their former habitations I said, and remove altogether the sting of the immigration problem. Reuben's reaction was instantaneous and violent.

'What has democracy to do with it? Do you imply by your statement that democracy is of a higher moral order than Christianity? No political or moral régime, which the modern, mediæval or ancient worlds has known has ever made any difference to Jewish destiny. Whether emperor, king, dictator, parliament, or baron – the brutally aggressive or subtly hypocritical kick to get them on the move again remained the same throughout. The tragedy was, and still is, that in time the victim himself became so hardened that only savage brutality made him cry out – but as to movement even subtle tricks were enough to set him trekking. But that is a long story.'

I did not press him any further for the moment. We had done a good day's work and I was content.

III

A few days later, on a wet autumn day, when low lying clouds and dripping ground mists made that gloomy atmosphere, so much dreaded by Prisoners of War, Reuben came to my room. Ted, the red-haired Australian, was with me busily engaged in coaxing our ersatz electric heater to produce a brew.

"Hello, Jack, Hello, Ted . . . I hope you'll get the brew going, as I am cold and could do with a nice cup of tea.'

Ted made some unprintable remark about German flex, and about the ungracious neighbours next door who liked butting in on our brewing time – thereby cutting off the current altogether. However, he eventually won through, and we settled down to enjoy the hot liquid. As cigarettes were then at a premium, everybody rolled his own, from a weird collection of fag-ends jealously hidden in any odd tin or cheese box.

In the course of a platitudinous conversation old Ted as was usual with him, dropped a brick . . . I suspected strongly that it was not mere accident. Ted, whenever he wanted to get some reaction from his friends – the English – was in the habit of quite innocently dropping a stone into a pool – leaving it to the ripples to do the splashing. His horsey face was at such moments innocence itself, and it gave the impression that its owner might be on the verge of tears, as soon as the effect of his mischief became apparent. While he was rolling a cigarette with his masterly fingers, which might make of a tin anything from an electric heater to a distiller, he proceeded to tell us of a trick played by an Australian immigration officer on an undesirable alien immigrant. A certain communist writer, Ted told us, arrived in a liner on the shores of Australia. The immigration officer in charge happened to know about Mr. Kish's views and activities, and thought that that gentleman should be refused permission to land. Legally it was a difficult procedure, since Mr. Kish appeared to have his papers in order, and to fulfil all the conditions demanded of him. The immigration officer suddenly remembered the literacy test. As Mr. Kish spoke and wrote several European languages, and as the regulations left a free hand to the immigration officer, the latter decided to test Mr. Kish in the Gælic language. Mr. Kish failed, of course, and the immigration officer with a wide grin on his face left the boat with a protesting Mr. Kish still on board. But there was still trouble ahead. Mr. Kish, a highly adventurous and forceful character, jumped into the sea, broke his leg in so doing, and was eventually rescued and put into a hospital on shore. Once on land Mr. Kish lost no time in communicating with friends and the progressive Press of the country began shouting blue murder. The affair became a public scandal, and although Mr. Kish was officially vindicated he had had in fact to leave the country. As soon as Ted mentioned the name – which meant nothing to me – Reuben's colour changed. He became – as was his habit when his sensitive corns were trodden on – red hot up to his hair roots, and turned a glassy stare on Ted. Reuben listened to the story without uttering a sound, and only the crushing of his half-finished cigarette betrayed a suppressed irritation. When Ted finished the story with a chuckle, Reuben, to my relief, chuckled with him.

'Very ingenious indeed for an immigration officer but, Ted, take it from me, the immigrants also know a trick or two, and in the battles royal fought between immigration officers who flatter themselves that they keep the keys of their respective countries, the immigrants, as often as not come out on the right side. It reminds me of the tiny fire brigade fighting the fires caused by a two thousand ton air raid, with a four inch hose. We know too well who laughs last in such a case. When people have to escape famine, gallows, auto-da-fés, concentration camps, and all the varied forms of persecution which the savage core of man can invent, then an immigration officer is to be pitied for the futile task which an unrealistic government lays on him. I don't envy the immigration officer his thankless task. I had a scrap or two with such officials, and can tell you they were hopelessly out-manœuvred, and this in a little country like Palestine, where control should be far easier than in the big countries.'

'Would it be too indiscreet to enquire', said Ted with a twinkle in his eye, 'how you came out from your encounters with the immigration officers.'

'I am afraid it is too long a story – for to understand how it happened that I became an immigrant, one must come to know the whole background of my people's migrations. My own little adventure is but a tiny . . . though I hope a final – offshoot, of migratory movements covering a period of over 2,500 years. The subject is too extraneous to be of much interest to both of you, and at any rate how could a full stomach share a body with a starved man?'

'Damn it, man,' – it was Ted who saw an opportunity slipping, 'you are mistaken there, Reuben. I do want to know, what is all this about the Wandering Jew. Quite a few German Jews came to Australia, and those I happened to come across were intelligent and decent folk, yet I think I may say it to you, and no offence meant, we would not like to see too many of them. I know what the square-headed blighters did to them, but well, the fact remains that wherever you go you come across the same thing; your people like wandering about and I do not say that I blame them.'

'In spite of all statements to the contrary,' replied Reuben, 'I maintain that the Jews less than any other people I know of, have never moved or migrated of their own volition. In fact,' he went on, 'I think the Jews are the most conservative people as far as migration is concerned, and even a superficial observer must agree. Every move for them is hazardous, breaks their strongly-knit family life, and exposes them to the strain of adaptation to an unknown environment. I studied the subject during my Berlin exile and have continued it now in captivity – but I failed to discover a single instance of voluntary Jewish migration. If anything, my people began moving always an hour after elementary foresight might have warned them. They migrated when forced to do so, but they had to be properly squeezed and kicked, before they shouldered their bundles. For a detached scholar it ought to be an intriguing subject, but it has always given me the cold shivers. I believe it was your compatriot John Bright who said that every generation stands on the shoulders of the preceding one, and sees farther. In the case of my people, it has always struck me that we used the shoulders of our ancestors in order to climb down and to see less. The experience of former generations was lost on us until quite recent times, when through the wrath of a slighted, completely assimiliated Western Jew, Dr. Herzl – a subject of the Austro-Hungarian Empire – we came to the conclusion, that to retrace our steps to our historical land was the answer to the never-ending perigrinations. Dr. Herzl put us at last on the shoulders of our fathers and let us catch a glimpse of the light in the East. I don't know how to set out on that sweeping journey, which must survey a matter of twenty-five centuries in order to give you an idea of what happened to that race, and how it came to be in the position in which it finds itself to-day.

'See if you can follow me through that crazy pattern, resembling nothing so much as the tangle of condensation strips intersecting vaporous lines, left in the skies after a furious battle. In our case we can at least see where it all began. Let us take a section of time, say a thousand years in length – beginning in the early eighth century B.C., and ending say with Constantine the Great. In terms of events pertinent to our subject, it begins with the first Assyrian deportation of Jews from Palestine, and ends roughly with Christianity becoming the official religion of the Roman Empire, which meant the end of the religious toleration granted by the pagans to the last remnants of the Jewish community in Palestine. Picture to yourself that section of time as something rugged and splintered at its edges, since it is arbitrarily broken away from its context. Well, all the empires of the ancient world – with mild exceptions in the case of the Persian Empire under

Cyrus (who even favoured a feeble attempt at restoration) – each in turn took a hand in clawing and tearing at the comparatively small body politic of the Jews, until Jewry in Palestine became almost extinct and scattered all over the civilized world, as it then was. It is the only period in the history of my people of which I feel – I am ashamed to say – almost chauvinistically proud. Deportation; auction on slave markets; massacres; whips, pogroms and forced worship of idols and Cæsars; all this and more descended on a community which probably never numbered more than 2-3 million souls, and notwithstanding they fought back – savagely and ruthlessly at times – and clung to their soil. Needless to say, the section of the population which bore the brunt of the struggle and stayed on to the end of those thousand years, were our Galilean highlanders and the Judæan hillfolk. As late as the end of the second century A.D. – after more than eight hundred years of this ferocious uprooting process, carried on by the mightiest empires of the day – we still read of widespread revolts against the Roman rule, at a time when the national body was already dissipated. Those were the last flickers of their heroic struggle, although one may doubt whether such a fight to the last could have been justified on political grounds. Many men of the time, wise and politically broad-minded, saw in such a fanatical policy, no more than national suicide, although it is difficult to judge whether a policy of compromise and resignation to the civilization of the conquerors would have secured the national and political survival of the Jewish state and culture.

'I am afraid I let myself go too much. What is of relevance to our story is the question of what happened to those hundreds of thousands of deported Jews, to those sold as slaves; and to those Jews of the town who left the country when they could no longer stand up to the exaction of conquerors, and of the patriotic partisans alike. If we hark back we shall see and hear them trekking in overland caravans and in sea-going craft to the north and west of Palestine. They spread as far as the Caucasus on one side, and as far as Rome, Spain and even Gaul on the other. We see them moving in compact bodies of families, or even whole communities; and furthermore we see the friendly and generous welcome offered to them by the natives in these distant lands. For the new arrivals – although Asiatics and barbarians in the eyes of the near-Eastern, and especially so in the eyes of Hellenic and Roman society – were by no means to be despised. The immigrants brought with them a high level of craftmanship, their proletariat was made up of hardy workers and hill-farmers, and their intelligentsia achieved fame in many sciences of their time – medicine, cartography, philosophy, languages and the art of writing. Their men of business, schooled in a country which lay on the main route of the East to West trade, were well grounded in financial and trade dealings on an international scale. Furthermore, as a result of family and racial ties, they provided agencies in all parts of the civilized world, and transactions made through them, opened to the producer or exporter world-wide contacts. The immigrants prospered, and as true Asiatics were highly prolific. In due course they were in a position to send money to Palestine, thereby assisting their compatriots in the prolongation of the struggle against the foreign, pig-eating conquerors. Should I have painted this picture of the first migration waves too brightly one must remember that it did not lack its sordid counterpart. The native populations – Asiatics, Greeks, Romans, Gauls – who welcomed the newcomers, soon tired of their alien, and to them, disgusting customs. They found them uncanny in their prosperity and religious practices, and, as soon as they had learned all the immigrants had to teach them the natives were increasingly irritated by the competition of the newcomers. The natives had another, and I think quite justifiable grudge against the War Lords and Governors of the subject populations who made clever use of the Asiatic Jews, they in their turn found in the Lords of the domain protection against the mob and fanatics, and repaid them by becoming their most reliable administrators, tax-gatherers and political emissaries. For the native people it was, of course, easier to hate the tool than its master and retaliation followed swiftly. But it was not before the Christianisation of the Greco-Latin world that the pent-up resentment of the natives against their Asiatic guests was released. There you are – by the time Christianity took on the imperial purple, and a new platonic philosophy, the Jewish exiles were already well established round the fringes of the Mediterranean, with as yet only a few slender tentacles, reaching out as far as the Black Sea to the East. But they remained Asiatics all through the first millenium of their Exile.'

Reuben checked himself here, to gather speed for the steep climb which lay before him. But before he could proceed, I was on him with a question, which his casual reference to the factional strife among the Jews in Palestine during the times of their hardest trials suggested to me.

'I understand from your words', I queried, 'that the process of the dispersal of the Jews from their homeland covered about a thousand years – at the end of which, all organised political and national life was finally crushed. Can you tell me what life was like in Palestine during these momentous centuries? I have nothing to go on in my attempt to visualise what it was like.'

'That is a very intelligent question, but you are mistaken if you think that you know next to nothing about it. You know, of course, all there is to know about it, but – owing to the way the bible, gospels, and in fact all ancient history is taught – you miss the time-setting of the events. The problem is certainly well worth considering, for it holds a unique fascination for every student of history and culture. For while the lifeblood of the nation was steadily dissipated, and while the intricate international power politics of the ancient world had their repercussions in fierce and relentless factional strife within, in fact while calamities befell the people century by century, a tremendous flowering in the intellectual and moral life of the country took place. During those fateful convulsions which wrecked the body, we look on breathlessly at the dazzling array of prophets; we meet the titanic intellectual struggle against Hellenism, we hear the scratching of the scribes on parchment as they compile, censor, and often corrupt, the texts which went into the making of the Bible; we follow the revolt against the town civilization by the Nazarenes; we watch the climax of almost unearthly humanitarian idealism embodied in Jesus of Nazareth, and we see the final and irrevocable rift between Pauline Christianity (making its peace with Empire and Neo-hellenism) – and Jewry. It was unquestionably the golden age of the race, paid for by the national and political ruin. The most precarious equilibrium, which it is the biological fate of man to have to maintain between the material world and the world of the spirit, a battle raging in every man's heart and in every society, was definitely lost.

'The intellectual and ethical outbursts, for instance, of the French and Russian revolutions, were almost, but not quite, paid for with national and material ruin. They escaped by a hairbreadth and eventually recovered their equilibrium. The Jews had poured out their souls with their national body – it took another two thousand years before even an attempt to restore the balance could be made. The story has been put in many words

and I am aware that mine are just as ineffectual as others, but
nevertheless the fact stands out clearly and unquestioned; the era
of the national and political ruin was also – and who can tell,
perhaps because of it – the pinnacle of the intellectual achievements of the Jewish race as such. And when it came to an end, it
saw the country in ruins, and its people dispersed round the shores
of the Mediterranean. There ends act one of the migration
drama.'

We had to break off, for our German lunch – millet porridge –
was at the door, and the remainder of my room mates came
bustling in.

IV

Although Reuben stayed in Berlin on two more occasions years
later – when he was in charge of rescue work for the German
Jews – the five or six months he spent there before his Aliyah to
Palestine he reckoned to be among the most productive months
of his intellectual growth. There was nothing to distract his concentration from the task he set himself. In Eastern Europe he had
never come across such opportunities. In the university for politics
and economics, and in its 'jumble of a library' he made his headquarters, from which he made frequent sorties into other faculties,
where the great teachers and professors of the time delivered their
lectures to a thirsty, and rather cosmopolitan crowd of half starved
students. In one of these lecture halls he met Sonia, the roving
daughter of a wealthy Jewish family, domiciled in a Scandinavian
country – who became his companion in the joys Berlin could
offer in 1926, which were all a couple of young and overflowing
hearts could desire. There were the, to them, unheard of luxuries
of Museums and art galleries to be visited, opera, symphony concerts conducted by Walther, Weingartner and others; Saturday
morning Bach and Brahms concerts in the cathedral; and rare
excursions to the Harz and Giant mountains. Much instructive
experience, and a good deal of fun, was also to be gained at the
public meetings and debates of the contesting political parties,
ending more often than not in free fights and police intervention.
Most of the meals – except for an occasional gala supper at a smart
restaurant, were prepared by Sonia on a little gas stove in her own
or Reuben's little dark back room, in the proletarian north quarter
of Berlin – money had to be kept for theatres and concerts – and

143

the raw material for the meals was chiefly supplied by bulky food parcels they received from home, and fruit and vegetables bought at the market stalls of broad-beamed Berliners. At least six hours a day followed by a couple of hours before retiring to bed in the early hours of the morning Reuben strictly devoted to the study of a bewildering array of bulky volumes. The first month or so he sunk himself in political history and economic theories. But he was soon – by a chance attendance at a lecture on geopolitics – attracted to another topic, to which he gave all his attention and study in the following months. The lecturer was a Professor Gold-schmidt, of distinctly non-Aryan appearance, whose fiery national-istic rhetoric and highly fashionable subject matter made him the lion of the student crowd. The lecture which turned Reuben's interest to the history of migrations and colonization movements, dealt with the colonial expansion of the British peoples. The pro-fessor, in his lecture, gave rise to hilarious uproars by his sallies against the Imperialism of the shopkeepers, in which to Reuben's surprise, the considerable group of English-speaking students took prominent part. Reuben, who expected a violent and scandalous reaction, was deeply impressed and confused by the way the English and Scottish students reacted to the professor's rather vulgar and offensive thrusts against their people. So when, in due course, Professor Goldschmidt found the opportunity to mention the 'gipsy wanderings of the hook-nosed mongrel race', Reuben, though blushing furiously, kept his own counsel, when the whole crowd gave vent to prolonged cheers. He went to hear the Pro-fessor again, on the migration of the German tribes and on their clashes with Roman and Slav. And here again the Professor had something to say about the invasion of Germany by the Jews, and their corrupting influence on the present state (1926) of the German nation. Reuben felt himself strongly attracted by the subjects which shed new light on the migrations of peoples, their colonising efforts, and in particular the peculiar story of Jewish wanderings. He made up his mind to devote himself entirely to the study of these subjects. Professor Goldschmidt proved himself a generous and helpful, if not unbiassed guide, and kept Reuben supplied with all available literature. Mommsen, Mayer, Haus-hofer, and several works on Jewish history, by Jewish and non-Jewish authors were now to be seen on his desk. Sonia was also drawn in to help, and in fact – not knowing how long he would have to stay in Berlin – he began shortly to work on a treatise dealing with a comparative study of Jewish and non-Jewish migrations. He never finished it, for after a few months he felt the call of Palestine so strongly as to abandon his research, and to embark immediately for the Middle East. Reuben managed, however, shortly after his arrival in the country, to publish in a local magazine a bulky investigation of the relation between imperialism and colonization in old and modern times. But life and hard work in Palestine, coupled with public duties in which Reuben became shortly involved, curtailed his longing to pursue the study of the subject any further. It was, he told me, only now – eighteen years later – in Germany again, but as a P.O.W., that he had taken up his research with the aid of as many books as he could obtain.

These details Reuben related to me when he saw a quizzical look on my face after our first talk on the migration problem of the Commonwealth, which he followed with his sensational exposure of the trends and peculiarities of the Jewish migrations. It was then that he gave me the stirring, if sweeping, account of 'the first thousand years' of the Jewish Diaspora. I don't mind admitting that the relation which Reuben established between the physical and political ruin of the Jewish race, and 'the unique flowering of its creative genius; unsurpassed ever since' struck me at first as bravado. But then, what objections could I make when some time later I discovered almost parallel remarks made by Lord Rosebery on a certain period of the history of the Scots. In an address on the peculiarities of Scottish history delivered in 1880, Lord Rosebery said among other things:

'Take for example this peculiarity, that Scotland, *while she had a history, developed a striking character but no material prosperity,* but from the moment she ceased to have a history, she developed a material prosperity so marvellous *as completely* to obliterate her national character. Until the Union of Crowns the Scots nation were only known as a turbulent race of hardy heroes – poor, indeed, but poor because they preferred poverty to dependence, and were willing to sacrifice their castles and their crops to prevent the invader having a home or subsistence on Scottish soil. All this is now forgotten' . . . and further on . . . 'the ancient reputation has been overlaid for two centuries with the reproach of avarice and the stigma of self-seeking.'

When I showed the quotation to Reuben, with the slightly malicious intention of debunking the historical uniqueness of the point he made, he stood pondering for a moment, and suddenly his face lit up in laughter.

'Look here, Jack,' he said, I have come to believe that the lost ten tribes must be looked for in the British Isles, preferably in Scotland! It is, indeed, a striking analogy but no more. For all kinds of disaster may overtake a people, but as long as that people is not expelled from its own country, the chance of recovery and of a new life is always at hand. Moreover, the Scots had England next-door – after all, not the worst neighbour to have. Hey? Well, nothing like it happened to us – once on the down slope, there was no halt. Wherever and whenever we managed to arrest our downward fall for a while, sure enough a subtle squeeze or a brutish kick would send us sliding again.'

With that remark Reuben came back to his tale. While I listened to the story, I came to accept Reuben's assertion that the experiences of the past were not impersonal things, but as alive to him as the adventures of his own lifetime.

'Well,' he continued aggressively, 'you, for instance, must possess a lively imagination in order to identify yourself with the Danes and Normans who jumped on to the shores of England. You require an even more fanciful imagination to recapture the atmosphere and actuality of the struggle between parliament and king. Such phases of your national history became overlaid with so many fresh, and much more modern events, that it remains of interest to the scholar or the novelist only. As against it, the history of my people of a hundred, a thousand or two thousand years ago has nothing alien or remote in it. It is just as clearly visible and pertinent to me, as Hitler's mobile gas chambers in Poland. All Jewish history follows one and the same law, particularly since the Jews acquired the most unfortunate epithet of "Europeans". I told you, didn't I, that up to Constantine's time they were recognised by all, and moreover by themselves, as Asiatics and as Jews. They suffered for it but they escaped self-deception, and did not presume on their neighbours by being accepted as co-nationals. The Jews in Rome, Athens, Tarsus and Morocco, did not call themselves Romans or Greeks except for a very few and did not expect others to take them as such. Long after St. Paul had given up the Jews, and had turned to the Gentiles, there came a change which, not being on Pauline lines, remained down to our times a tragic one; for the Jews were at last drawn into the circle of European civilization, at a time when that term meant the civilization of the Roman church. Merovingians and Carlovingians and even Charlemagne, the orthodox Christian, all encouraged the Jews to move deeper into Europe – away from the fringes of the Mediterranean. These rulers needed them badly in order to free themselves from the bonds of the clergy. They were the only literate class at hand to serve the temporal and spiritual interests of the monarchs. The new growing political and national states of Western and Central Europe – before and after the rule of Charlemagne – were in need of skilled craftsmen, businessmen, physicians, stewards, and men capable of performing state business at home and abroad. The Jews could do all of it and yet remain faithful and dependent subjects, to be balanced conveniently against the clergy barons inside the domain, and against the newly-acquired colonial peoples in the East. In turn the Jews were promised religious toleration, protection against their competitors, and needless to say material prosperity. Such alluring prospects for a people who had become more and more marked as outcasts among the true believers, started the migration of the Jews into Western and Central Europe, which under the Normans extended to the British Isles. In the course of five centuries the Jews became a European people, shedding their Asiatic garb and speech, and acquiring a new colloquial language, Yiddish, a corruption of medieval German.

'We may assume that a good many of the wealthy classes remained stubbornly aloof, as the decrees of the Lateran councils forbade Christians any kind of blood and business intercourse with the Jews. For the first time in their history, the Jews began to identify themselves with their hosts, calling themselves Germans, French, English, Spaniards, and incidentally adding to their Hebrew designations Christian and foreign family names. The German Emperor, Otto the Great, the founder of the "Drang nach Osten" school, found in his Jews a very useful tool for colonization and the subsequent subjection of the Bohemians and of the Danube peoples. Thus the Jews incurred the undying resentment of these peoples. Led by and often preceding the German arms the Jews pushed open the gate into Eastern Europe. We see them at the turn of the first Christian millenium migrating – as yet a slender trickle – into Eastern and South Eastern Europe. But such prosperous expansion and striking of roots was not destined to last. The blow, when it came, fell as a surprise and was exceeded in its deadliness only by Hitler Germany. That blow was struck first – you may be surprised to hear it – in England and by a ruler who was one of the greatest English statesmen of the Middle Ages – Edward I.'

'So it was he who expelled the Jews from England in 1290?'

'Yes, he did, but not without great searching of heart even for so remarkable a personality. Edward I, you may be surprised to hear such a paradoxical assumption, anticipated part of the modern Zionist answer seven centuries before the Jews themselves came to think about it, and before another British philosopher statesman gave his Government's sanction to a radical settlement of the very problem with which Edward was confronted. Edward thought to appease the anger of church and mob against the Jews, by a radical change in their economic life. He perceived quite rightly that the concentration of the Jews in towns and in business was to blame for the resentment demonstrated against them by his people. He tried, therefore, to open for them the feudal countryside and the professional guilds. He failed as was inevitable, and as many similar experiments have since failed, because the people objected to the presence of the Jews among them, not only for economic reasons; and as far as truly economic interests went, they refused simply to have the experience of their townspeople repeated amongst their countryfolk. When Edward realised that his constructive policy had failed, he would have no more compromise, but expelled the Jews. As the refugees, laden with their few, but highly valuable possessions – they were not the first generation to realise that people liable to be kicked out at a moment's notice will do wisely to store their wealth in small but precious goods (which, by the way, is a good example of how national characteristics develop) – arrived on the Continent, expelled from an England even then of high standing in the eyes of the civilized world, it was reason enough for the Continental rulers to do the same. On the Continent the stage had long been set for it, and some thorough work in true Continental fashion had already been done. The crusades, which began roughly two centuries before Edward's expulsion act, had blazed a blood trail across the Jewish communities in the Rhine and Danube valleys, and a violent outburst of persecution and of forced conversion preceded and followed in the train of the crusaders, which almost, if not quite, put an end to Western European Jewry. Hundreds of thousands of them perished – some scholars put the figure at about 1,350,000 – only a few communities survived in the West, as a result of the vigorous protection lent them by enlightened Bishops – but the mass of the people saved their lives and conscience by fleeing eastwards. It was their good fortune to find in the Polish dynasties, and nobles, and in Turkey a haven of refuge. The Jews were much in demand here, and for the same reason as they were a few centuries ago in the West. From Poland of Cazimir the Great, and from the Ottoman empire under Saladin, the Jews pushed on even further eastwards into Russia, and to the South East into the Balkans. The Crusades made the Jews an Eastern European people, by forcing them out of the West. It was here that the Jews increased and multiplied in geometrical progression. Well – getting down from the big to the small issues – that is how some of my ancestors, after having added to their Ben Shalom or Ben Salomon a German family name, had eventually landed themselves between Dniester and Pruth.'

This is as far as I managed to keep Reuben going. The remainder, and the finish, appeared of little interest to him. He said it made him sick and feverish to repeat the same blood tale all over again, because the West to East migration ended in the same disaster as the previous South to North migration, i.e., from the fringes of the Mediterranean into Western and Central Europe. When the reformation swept away the old prejudices, the Jews again picked up their bundles and returned to the West (and with Cromwell's warm approval, also came back to England). When the possibilities of America became known they streamed there in their millions from Western and Eastern Europe. And when the French revolution declared the Rights of Man and emancipated the Jews – soon to be followed by all the other West European countries – the Jews believed that now the millenium of the brotherhood of men had dawned and all racial and religious discriminations would vanish for ever. But scarcely had one set of prejudices been discarded, when a new pest of nationalistic chauvinism reached its climax with the Nazi savagery – and made Europe – East and West – one huge concentration and death camp for the Jews.

'I am not framing any charges', he cried out to me with marked agitation, 'against the Gentile world. One has to admit that the Gentiles have used – and are still using – the same methods against their co-religionists as against us. But the sojourn of the Jews among the Gentiles has been a long drawn out tale of misery and disaster, in which a few phases only stand out as shining examples of the humanitarian virtues.

'But what shall I say about my own unteachable, blind and dogged people who would never learn? Every flash of new humanitarian spirit, and every spark of new social and ethical conception has thrown them into fits of illusion and self-deception. In the end whatever turn they took led only to the same cul de sac. They remained Jews, and the world never forgot it for long, although at times it showed them a grinning and amiable face of toleration. Oh! toleration – is there anything more degrading? And that is the most enlightened attitude we could expect in the Diaspora!

'Do you still wonder that my generation was willing to pay any price to escape the well-meant tolerance? – to hell with all the blessings of tolerance, sympathy, hypocrisy and all the offspring of their family! Give me some space and environment of my own – I hope we shall not make a mess of it again.'

There was nothing more to be gained from him. He hurried off and left me standing, obviously ashamed of his emotions – for he never trusted an Englishman to have sentiments and emotions like any other human being. And yet had he given me time I could have consoled him with the words of an Englishman:

World on worlds are rolling ever
From creation to decay,
Like the bubbles on a river,
Sparkling, bursting, borne away.

I doubt, however, whether mere words, be it sublime verse or rustic prose, had it in their power to quell Reuben's revolt against the tragic vicissitudes of his people's history.

V

Reuben could not stay on in Berlin. His passport for one thing, would become invalid in another three month's time. He knew now that Berlin had given him the means to pursue his intellectual interests unaided by the guiding hands of professors. He knew that all he required now were books and personal experience in political life, to which both ambition and glowing interest kept calling him. He had parted from his friends when they went to Palestine, and had remained behind for the sake of the movement. The little group of sixty odd members had erected its tents in Haifa, and was working on road construction and drainage of the swamps in the Haifa bay. The situation in Palestine – according to all reports – was rather critical. With the cessation of immigration, an economic crisis had sprung on the country. The funds of the Jewish Agency were low, and private capital sat on the fence, to await political developments before it proceeded with its investments. The economic and political depressions lay heavily on the young immigrants, who after years of training for, and dreaming of Palestine, found themselves partially unemployed, half-starving, and consequently deeply unnerved. Reuben, reading the letters from his friends telling of their harsh experiences, felt mad with apprehension. Here he sat, wallowing in the luxury of books and concerts, and there his comrades were, going through what might be the most critical stages of their lives, the stepping down from the heights of idealistic longing to the drab struggle for daily bread. He must join them, but how? There was no legal entry into the country. So what to do? He would smuggle himself into Palestine, as many thousands starting with the 'Singer of Zion', the famous poet Jehuda Halevy, before and after him had done, and would be doing. He felt no pangs of conscience in breaking the law.

'You cannot break a law which in itself represents a flagrant breach of the constitution of your country' – he stated mildly in answer to my query. 'What did your ancestors do when the constitution and Magna Charta were infringed upon by your hereditary kings? Whom of the contesting parties has history acquitted? Well, the constitution of Palestine – your legal title to govern the country – guaranteed that Jewish immigration would be facilitated by the mandatory power. If you insist on having my credentials as a law-abiding citizen, here they are. In fact I did not care two hoots about the law. My right to go to Palestine was morally unshakable. I knew I was not going to harm anybody. I was going to live my own life and redeem the man-made desert and pestilential marshes of the country. I knew then, and I feel it even more deeply at present, that there is scarcely a right in the world with a more profoundly legal and moral core, than my immigration to Palestine.'

Reuben joined a group of Halutzim who tried to make their way into the country by procuring a tourist visa. In such cases if they overstayed the three months touring limit, they forfeited their deposit. The visas were eventually obtained, and after a dismal journey over the Mediterranean waters the liner came in sight of Haifa. Reuben had no eyes for the sights of a Mediterranean cruise, for he kept worrying over his coming ordeal, the interview with that bogey known as the immigration officer. His forebodings proved to be justified. The officials of the Palestine immigration department refused to believe that Reuben was a plutocratic student tourist. Although many of his comrades bluffed their way through, Reuben's bluff – not very convincing even to himself – was called. He was turned down, and told to go back on the same liner.

'Believe me, Jack, it was one of the most bitter moments of my life. There in front of me stretched the Carmel and over on the shore I could see my friends loading and unloading merchandise on lighters. My binoculars even revealed to me Jewish labourers on the scaffolding of buildings inside the town. I was, however, most deeply agitated by the sight of a man sweeping a road leading down to the port. A Jew, sweeping with a steady harmonious stride like any road cleaners I had seen in other parts. I felt dizzy with pride and satisfaction. I said to myself – I did not dream of Utopia, here they are, the sons of the shopkeepers and pawnbrokers, the University students – here they do the manual tasks with their own hands. That helped me tremendously to overcome the hurt to my dignity when a British Official backed by his policeman sent me coolly back whence I came. I cried out to a passing stevedore quite unknown to me: "I shall come back, I shall be here shortly – police or no police".'

And come he did in a fortnight's time. When the liner dropped anchor in a Syrian port Reuben managed to slip ashore. Once on land he began his quest for a guide to lead him over the Lebanon, and Galilean ranges into Palestine. Things looked none too cheerful, until Reuben chanced on a professional gang of Arab smugglers. A Jewish family with whom he had found shelter advised him strongly against trusting his life and passage to such a disreputable body of men. But there was nothing for it – the risk had to be taken.

'For,' he argued, 'my adventure seemed to me the mildest of risks, compared with others undertaken by thousands of my predecessors on their way to Palestine. Under the Turkish rule no Jewish immigration to Palestine was permitted. Nevertheless, thousands and thousands filtered in by making use of every loophole which the law afforded; not only young Jews but even old men, who came to Palestine to rest their bones in the sacred soil, braved all the dangers of sea voyages on boats of pirates and smugglers – many of whom found their grave in the sea, or on the beach, robbed and killed for their few possessions. During the reign of anarchy and civil war in the Russia of 1917-24 thousands of our boys and girls made their way to Palestine, covering 1,000 and 1,500 miles on foot over the ice and snow of the Tauranian and Armenian mountains. How many of them lost their lives from sheer exhaustion, or from coming in between the fire of the fighting camps, we shall never know. The Odysseys of the German Jews and other refugees were then still in the womb of time. But I knew enough of the deeds and heroism of my contemporaries to approach my own little smuggling affair in good heart. What it boils down to, Jack, is just a repetition of a very old experience. Those officials who are put by their Governments to fight men and women craving for a bit of land and for a scrap of human dignity are to be pitied. I once felt bitterly about them – to-day I am just sorry for those officials, for having to make a living by performing such an ignominious duty. I also had a duty to myself and to my people to perform – and that's all there was to it.'

Reuben, clad in Arab garb on top of his European suit, was put on a donkey, after he had spent a whole day with an Arab family of about eighteen souls, all in one, smoky, all-purpose room A bright moon lit the caravan of donkeys and camels as it picked its way over precipitous tracks. They rode and tramped – Reuben had something special to say about the straw saddle, and for the entire donkey species – the whole night. Twice they were hailed by French gendarmerie and once by a Palestine police patrol, Reuben made himself small on these occasions – but what he actually feared most was to see the whole gang arrested should their contraband be discovered. However, nothing untoward happened, except that the Arabs halted twice to search Reuben's pockets for an extra bakshish. They did not find much in them. When the sun began pouring down her early blessings on a barren landscape, an Arab approached Reuben and told him casually, pointing to the ground:

'Hada Palestine.'

'It electrified my whole being', he concluded his tale. 'At first I could not believe it, and I made him repeat it so many times that the puzzled Arab began to look at me gravely. You must understand Jack, how I felt. For about twelve years I had done nothing but talk and dream of Palestine. And now to find myself there in Arab guise, and after a fantastic night march with all my limbs aching, struck me as slightly ludicrous. It must have been the anticlimax of anxiety and worry. I returned the borrowed Arab outfit to my guides, gave them an extra pound, which I produced, to their surprise, from my boots, and thanking them profusely I made my way to the nearest town. In a few hours time a taxicab deposited me, still in my dandy tourist outfit, at the camp of my friends. A few more minutes and I had created a record in handshakes and kisses of welcome. But there was as yet no respite for me. Before I could say "Jack Robinson", Deb, the devil – remember the consumptive snobbish Deb – now utterly transformed, carried me off to inspect her offspring. She, Deb, had become the first mother, and was she proud! For there in a meshwire cage, roasting in the sun, lay Rayah, the first daughter of our community.'

'Well, say something you boor', cried Deb beaming all over her impish face.

'My tongue was an unwieldy lump of flesh. But at last it came out. "Deb," I said, "your Rayah won't have to worry about immigration officers" – sealing that silly statement with a resounding kiss, pressed on a befuddled Deb.'

PART THREE

THE WORKER

CHAPTER ONE

A THEORY OF COLLECTIVISM

THE COLLECTIVE GROUP Reuben had joined on his arrival in Haifa was one of the many communal groups then scattered all over the country; some had been in the country for years and others were only recently founded. They all aspired to settle on land acquired by Zionist funds for the reconstruction of the Jewish National Home! But as funds were not sufficient to satisfy all the aspirants, colonization could not keep pace with the growth of communal and co-operative groups whose members were clamouring for settlement on the land. It might take as long as five years or even longer before a group would climb to the top of the roster to be rewarded by the lease of land, and the indispensable initial credits for the building of its settlement.

Until that longed-for moment arrived, when the feet of the pioneer actually trod the soil of his future homestead, every group had to make a living as best it could by hiring itself out to any employer at hand. The organisation and easy mobility of a collective group made it the ideal instrument for undertaking all kinds of public works, such as the drying of the many malaria-swept marshes of the country, the construction of roads, irrigation and town building schemes, and other big constructive projects. Wherever such work was available, many groups, or more often detachments from the mother units, would pitch their tents and remain until the work had been completed. The chief employers for such large-scale undertakings were the Zionist land and colonization corporations or private companies like the Palestine Electric Company, municipal corporations and occasionally the Palestine Government. But whereas the Jewish employers paid an adequate wage allowing for the standard of living of the European immigrant, the Government adhered to a wage and to general social conditions, fair enough for the Arab proletariat, but quite inadequate even for the simplest needs of a European labourer.

When Reuben got acquainted with the conditions in the country, particularly as far as employment was concerned, for which his own group served as a fair example, he came to realise that even such lowly paid work as that offered by the Government was scarce. Indeed, the economic depression was such that thousands of unemployed subsisted solely on the dole paid to them from the Zionist purse, since the Government itself felt free of any obligations towards the Jewish immigrants. After much pressure, and diplomatic representations, the Government had eventually consented to employ a few hundred Jewish labourers on special public work schemes designed for the purpose of relieving unemployment. For the remainder, the Zionist authorities had to share the burden of unemployment with the Jewish Labour Federation, known by friend and foe as HISTADRUTH, doing all the ingenious scheming and executing of plans for improving the situation. When the demoralizing ineffectiveness of the dole system became apparent, Labour laid down the drastic policy of 'Work And No Dole', which was enthusiastically supported by the unemployed themselves. Accordingly all moneys made available for the dole – one shilling a day per head – were converted into work, and three working days a week distributed among the unemployed.

The funds available for the payment of the dole were quite insufficient to produce three working days a week for the thousands of unemployed; consequently the Zionist authorities made an offer to public corporations, City bodies, and private investors to lend them money at a nominal rate of interest for payment of wages if they provided their own capital for the cost of materials, tools, etc. Organised public opinion and even direct action by the unemployed was brought to bear on corporations which were in possession of the necessary funds but who hung back owing to the general depression, in itself largely the result of the Government's policy. A central 'Depression Fighting Board', to which industrialists, planters, Labour and Municipalities were requested to send their representatives, was formed to consult the Jewish Agency on the schemes proposed. Thanks to these measures, the stagnation was eventually replaced by steadily growing economic activity which defeated the crisis in the end and forced the Government to re-open the gates of Palestine to the Jewish pioneers.

But that came later – very much later – in the meantime Reuben was helping to combat these difficulties. His community was fighting hunger with all the resources of youth; in the first year after his arrival in the country, the daily expenditure per head of the community never exceeded one shilling. As that 'statistical shilling' had to provide in the first instance for the babies, nursing mothers and the sick, the average expenditure for the 'normal member' of the community amounted only to a fraction of the shilling. Under the stress of such trying circumstances of unemployment, sickness, want, and all the other accompanying evils of economic chaos, the collective group proved its unchallenged superiority over any other way of life. The individualistic labourer who lived on his own, plagued by unemployment, sickness, and the misery of his pale offspring and overcome by despair for the cause in which he came to the country, would either retire crushed into his garret or whatever shelter he could find, or join the swelling numbers of those who spat into the face of all the ideals and revolutionary hopes which had induced them in the past to burn the bridges behind them. The collective effort on the other hand made it at least possible to shield the babies and the infirm from complete destitution by pooling every penny earned and by the economy possible in catering for larger numbers. The possession of a camp of their own – although consisting mainly of old army tents and a few ramshackle wooden huts, reserved for the communal institutions and the invalids – provided them with a home, clean and well looked after by those whose turn it was to stay at home. Thus even the unemployed had some occupation.

Perhaps Reuben's contention, which I have just put into my own words, will be further clarified if I acquaint the reader with the general make-up of a collective group similar to that which Reuben had joined. I am not certain whether any definition of principles and organisation will do justice to the subject, nor can I be sure that Reuben's coaching will save me from misrepresenting its true character. For I am quite aware of the fact that the collective way of life consists of more than a set of principles and various mechanistic devices.

Looking at it from the outside one is naturally struck by its most outstanding characteristic, the absolute renunciation of private property by all members of the collective group: Except for a few knick-knacks of furniture, room decorations, and other personal possessions such as watches, books, musical instruments, which are in the private domain of the individual, all resources appertaining to production and distribution, including the fruit of the individual's labour and the accrued profits, are the property of the community as a whole. The other fundamental element which is peculiar to the Palestinian collective movement lies, as Reuben explained, 'in the organic, and truly communistic principle of distribution, as opposed to the technical principle applied, for instance, in Russia.' The slogan of Palestinian collectivism reads: 'From everybody according to his faculties – to everybody according to his needs.' This means that every member of the community contributes to the common purse to the best of his ability, while the commune in turn distributes the fruit of the total effort according to the needs of the individual. The scale of distribution is not determined by the skill, talent or efficiency of the individual – the basis of distribution being his needs and not his merit as a bread-earner. The needs of the individual are assessed by committees which dispose of the funds allocated for the various purposes by the budget of the collective. The upbringing and education of the children are the responsibility of the community and not of the parents; while the parents follow their normal occupations the children are cared for by trained nurses and teachers. The decision of selecting a child for a specialised higher education lies with the community – acting on the advice of its educational council – and not with the parents. To quote Reuben's simile: 'the prescription of a medicine for the child lies with the doctor and nurse and not with the mother'.

'What are the parents for?' I asked in jest.

'To produce children', replied Reuben with a marked lack of humour – 'and the more the better – and to give them all the parental love and friendship of which they are capable; because for that no substitute will ever be found. But of the feeding of babies, their upbringing and education, the average parent knows just as much as of infantile diseases; such problems are the concern of experts – the trained nurse and the teacher. The parents are, of course, entitled to watch and criticise and to put forward their views on the subject, like any other member of the community.'

That was Reuben's point of view – remarkably akin, I thought, to the ideas which have created the public schools in England. In Reuben's case, however, such an educational system is an integral part of the collective community, and has the advantage of not depriving the children of contact with their parents for the best part of the year. What is otherwise a privilege of the wealthy classes becomes here a basic element of a proletarian society in being.

The management of the affairs of the collective is placed in the hands of executive officers and committees elected by the general assembly for the duration of one year. Officials who are a success in their offices, the secretary, treasurer, agricultural manager or whatever they may be, can be re-elected for another term, but as the collective is – I think – rather over-jealous in matters of official-dom it does not favour permanency in office. It is a prevailing custom to have, as far as possible, every member of the community serving on a committee to which he is best suited by inclination or by the actual task he performs. Every man or woman on joining the collective is a probationer for at least six, but no more than twelve months. After that period if the candidate has found the way of life suitable for him, he will apply to become a member of the collective. The assembly will either accept or reject the application (by a majority vote), after a free debate on the suitability of the candidate has taken place. If a candidate decides to leave the collective, or if his application is rejected, all his possessions and capital are returned to him; but once a member of the community, he forfeits all right to have his investments re-funded should he change his mind and leave. Reuben justified the apparent harshness of the measure by pointing out that the refunding of money already invested would upset the whole economic structure of the community. As every member of the collective is free to leave whenever he so desires, the community would be subjected to a permanent feeling of uncertainty about its investments and its economic position. In practice, I under-stand, the question is of little moment, because only a small fraction of the people who join the communal groups bring any considerable amount of capital with them.

So much I gathered from Reuben on the general framework of a Palestinian collective; it would appear that such an organisation is eminently suitable for a pioneering life under the very trying conditions of a country which is half wilderness and populated by a people with a low standard of living. In fact, pioneers of all times and in all parts of the world have known the stage of col-lective or co-operative organisation in one way or another – but there has always come a time when they reverted to a 'normal' individual way of life, becoming the masters of their property and the fruits of their labour.

What then are the incentives and inducements, which have kept alive the pioneering spirit in a considerable section of the Jews in Palestine, although the actual stage of pioneering was over for

L

them? Personally, I could find no other explanation than the idealistic ethical motives which appear so strongly in Reuben and his generation. And when I ventured to assert, that only saintly people dedicated to the realisation of such a way of life would be capable of maintaining such a society Reuben refuted it point blank.

'Your argument, Jack, sounds conventional and unreal, to me at any rate,' he stated pontifically, 'there are no more saints in our communities than in ordinary villages anywhere else in the world. Like myself, all my friends there' – here he pointed longingly to the East – 'are, I hope, normal human beings beset with ethical scruples and selfish greed, with ideals and a good deal of counter-acting inertia, in short, the usual mixture of good and evil which goes to make up the average human character. The one thing I will grant you is that our people are unquestionably superior to their fellow workers and peasants in the world in one way – that is in their standard of education. By this I do not mean teaching in schools alone – although it is an important educational factor, but above all I mean the education which lay behind the movement for which I worked and lived. I believe that our youth movements fermenting as they were under the stress of life in Europe, have instilled in us a new understanding of ourselves. It was self interest viewed from an unconventional and intellectual angle which made us adherents of the collective life.

'Although you and many others understand Idealism to be the key of one's approach to life, it is not so. I doubt very much whether Idealism strictly speaking can ever become a stable basis for the maintenance of a society. Idealism certainly has it in its power to fight inertia and convention, and since even revolutionary ideas sooner or later become a conservative reality – a strong dose of ambitious idealism in individuals and groups would be salutary for every type of society. But many experiments in the past – remember Owen's high-spirited attempts in your country and in America – the Tolstoian social experiments in pre-revolutionary Russia, the religious communities in America, etc., have proved beyond doubt that Idealism, divorced from the consciously perceived self interest of men, may occasionally give birth to a new social structure, yet it cannot maintain it. In fact we need not go so far back to prove our point. The utter failure of purely idealistic movements – in which I include the main religions of mankind – which have tried hard to make men live up to standards set by them can only be explained by the fact that they have ignored the limits set to the idealistic factor in mens' lives. You must be aware of the fact that the codes – religious, institutional and philosophical – devised to make man conscious of his neighbour, and which are thereby altruistic, have indeed produced a number of palliatives but have effected little change in his character and social aspirations. The heavenly reward promised to the saintly poor made some docile and subservient to the rich and mighty, but it had no real power to stop the scramble for the golden bowl on earth, which has remained throughout the pervading note of all known civilizations. We know of many personalities who have lived up to an ascetic ideal, scorning to besmirch themselves with earthly riches, but I know of no society which has made of altruism a basis for the life and work of its members. All the rewards – heavenly or earthly – which such creeds have promised, and although millions of men and women have believed in them, have been of no avail. Self interest, the shape and expression of which has varied with the conventions and civilizations of the age – has triumphed in the end, and the men of God, the law givers and the leaders of society have been forced to surrender to it.'

'If self-interest is destined to triumph,' I protested, 'then we may as well give up all hope of ever creating a new and a better world.'

'I maintain', cut in Reuben severely, 'that self-interest has triumphed so far, and will triumph for ever and that is the reason for my social optimism and for my belief in the communal society in Palestine. I declare that the fatal dualism as expressed by the alleged eternal and irreconcilable conflict between the evil which is self-interest and the ethereal glory which is disinterestedness or altruistic idealism – that dualism so stubbornly maintained by theologians, philosophers, statesmen and moralists is a dark alley from which there is no way out. I further venture to maintain that if a high social morality were incompatible with the self-interest of man it would never come to govern our society, and neither mystic rewards in heaven nor political régimes on earth would ever succeed in establishing it. A society which does not satisfy the self-interest of its members, and offers them instead ideals of love and self-sacrifice, exists only by the exercise of brute, if often veiled, force by those whose self-interest is more than satisfied. Such a society however, has no claim to be regarded as a free society. Our communal settlements in Palestine which are free societies by virtue of their being voluntary, have survived because they are designed to satisfy the self-interest of all their members; had they been built on airy idealisms they would have failed ignominiously in less than a lifetime. If they offered their members only the satisfaction of living a heroic life of self-sacrifice, they would have been crushed by the first impact with the attractions of town life and the seductive rewards of the life of the Capitalist Society round about us. The individualistic basis of capitalistic society – which I regret to say is still the way of life of the majority of Palestinian Jewry – would have overthrown our collective communities long ago had we not found an answer to the vital instinctive urge of self-preservation which more than anything else dominates the life of men. So, Jack, if you still maintain that our heads are in the skies nevertheless do not forget that our feet are firmly planted on the ground. The communal society has proved to be the ideal social organisation for the satisfaction of the self-interest of the Jewish pioneers in Palestine. The chimerical conflict between self-interest and common-weal has no meaning for us – because the one is in itself unthinkable without the other. Having unravelled that knot our communities have emancipated themselves from religious and philosophical falsehoods, and become free and capable to take the lead in the struggle for the building of the Jewish National Home in Palestine with the object of blending "self" and "common" into one natural and social whole.'

I could not reconcile myself with Reuben's theory of collectivism – it was certainly original, but was it true? His way of emphasising and glorifying self-interest was incongruous looked at in the light of his own life story. Was it disillusionment infused by the none too gentle bumps which a real Palestine had administered to him? But to turn to the argument itself. If self-interest of the individual is to be the criterion in the struggle between our materialistic greed and our religious and ethical scruples, I asked myself, how then is one to believe in a new and better world, particularly in a socialistic society which, I knew, was a firm belief of Reuben's.

'I am sorry, Reuben, but I fail to follow your arguments', I said at last apologetically. 'You want me to believe that your communal life was nothing but an expedient to serve your own ends. That is to say that your people agreed to renounce property and the fruit of their labour for the love of their own selves? I don't think you can mean it!' Reuben remained unshaken.

'The trouble is', he replied in a more conciliatory tone, 'that you and I approach the subject from a different angle. You take it for granted that the true compensation for a man's efforts and talents is money; money or its material equivalents; it is the conventional attitude of our civilization, which the better part of the religious and ethical movements have since tried to humanise somewhat. The fact is that money is indeed the means by which food, clothing, shelter, culture, rank, a pew in Church or Synagogue, are bought; the best which religious and moral philosophies and creeds could do against it, was to wring from it a fraction for cold, unfelt charity. In order to mitigate the obvious evils which have resulted from the quest for property, human society has invented from the earliest dawn of mankind the threats of the brimstone and hell fire, and alternatively the rewards of paradise. You cannot even pretend that such methods have succeeded, although the vast majority of mankind – past and present – has accepted and submitted to such ideas. The reason for the failure to convert man to a higher standard of morality and a better social conscience is to be found, we are told, in the archaic cliché that man's core was evil and corrupt. Well, Jack, I venture to suggest that man is not evil and corrupt, but that the analysis of his nature and the means employed for his betterment have been and still are, to say the least, misplaced and misjudged. As everyone can see for themselves it is man's self-interest which guides him to seek the shelter of the social organism. His life, prosperity, the education of his children, the field for the exercise of his gifts, the enjoyment of art and culture, his security, his conscience, his work and daily bread – all depend largely on the community. My proposal is then, to make the structure of the society conform to the inveterate instincts of self-preservation of the individual – and no threats nor heavenly allurements will then be required to make us consciously and willingly love our neighbours as ourselves. The "love your neighbour" commandment taken as a moral, or religious postulate carries little weight and no conviction – but for serving the self-interest of each of us it is indispensable and to-day, I think, also indisputable. I propose then humbly to mould our social life on such a philosophy – which has the merit of not being speculative, but a simple self-evident truth, crying out to us from wherever human beings work and strive. I propose to you to adopt such a creed because it is one with our instincts and with our reason. The futile battle against human nature would then come to an end, and the creation of the *"common wealth"* would finally begin. Is it not a fact – demonstrated by the whole course of our history – that man's self-interest urges him on to more and more complex forms of communal responsibility and thereby to a higher social morality?'

'Were it as you say', I replied, feeling less sure of myself, 'our personal contribution to the common-weal would be given as a matter of course, and it would be unnecessary to wrest it from us by threat of brimstone or by the truncheon of a policeman. I fail to discover that man was ever a willing member of a community. He was forced into it – be it by magic formulæ or more mundane means. How do you reconcile that fact', I asked Reuben, rather impatiently I fear, 'with your argument?'

'If you believe that to be true', he rejoined the contest with cold fury, which made his speech unsteady, 'it is easy to visualise the picture books which have suggested to you such an idea of human nature. There is – I can see it – the raging mountain of Sinai, perched menacingly over the Israelite crowd huddled in fear at its feet, ready to bury them alive on the spot, should they hesitate to submit to the decalogue. Had it not been for that divine threat, we are ordered to believe, the people of Israel, and with them the whole world thereafter, would have continued to live in savagery. Next there is, I should say, the picture of the slave, declared free by his benevolent master, refusing the boon conferred on him with the cry: "I love thee my master – I do not want to become free". In this picture-thought freedom is forced on us just as in the first picture, where social morality had to be instilled into the Israelites through the agency of a fire-spitting and rocking mountain. Then comes, I guess, the picture of the benevolent Lord, having to use a police squad in order to transfer his tenants from a grimy slum to a modern, steel and glass palace. Then there is the Newgate of old to make people pay their debts to their neighbours, and courts-martial to make us serve our country, and ex-communication or the stake to make us pious and faithful. These pictures, impressed on our minds since earliest babyhood, are responsible for the views we hold – much more than we care to admit.

'And if you ask for facts – well, tell me what have been the incentives and aims of all mass movements, revolutions, and social conflicts, down to the clamour for the Beveridge security scheme? Were all these collective actions, undertaken by the masses of the

people, aimed at a higher social responsibility or at a lesser one?
Are those the symptoms which you call on to support your contention that the people had to be compelled to live together, and
to bear their share for the common-weal?'

'You could have saved your trouble, Reuben', I broke in on his
passionate recital. 'Adam Smith has said it before you, and with
greater simplicity. Let the individual alone, he urged, and things
will adjust themselves without any interference from state or
society; in fact you only restate the hoary policy of *laissez-faire*.
Left to itself – self-interest played the devil with all values for
which it is worth while to live and strive. Have we not agreed
that the selfishness of individuals and classes has wrecked the
happiness of our society?'

'I am sorry, Jack, that we appear to be at cross purposes.'
Reuben still refused to acknowledge defeat. Although physically
exhausted he pursued his course vigorously. 'Let me deal first with
the term selfishness which has crept into our conversation. Selfishness is – it must be clear to you – not identical with self-interest.
It is related to it say, like prostitution to love or racialism to race.
In other words it is an abomination, a perversion of a vital human
necessity. Selfishness is a parasite sapping the life-blood of self-
interest. I hope that we are agreed on that point. Now as to your
very pertinent remark about the economic theory of a brilliant
Scotsman – well I am not ashamed to be in his company, because
Adam Smith's fundamental assumption was, as I understand it,
correct. I agree with him that no conflict exists between the self-
interest of the individual and the total economic interest of the
society. In one respect he failed however, and those who have
parroted the Master have sharpened his failure into disaster. He
failed, I believe, because he did not appreciate the intricate and
complex problem concerning the adjustment of the interests of
the individuals. The High Priests of economy made of that
question an esoteric mystery, beyond human control one might
say; whereas the High Priests of the Church made of religion a
well adjusted and centrally controlled business. Less harm would
have been done if religion had adopted the *laissez-faire* of
economy and if economy had adopted the universally controlled
catholicity of the Church. In short, the problem of our life is not
how to combat self-interest but how to harmonise. If harmony
be the social condition necessary for a functioning economy, then
competition is certainly not the means by which it may be

achieved. Could you expect, for instance, that an orchestra consisting of many different instruments should play in competition – can you envisage such an arrangement producing a symphony. Everybody agrees that for the performance of a symphony there must be gifted musicians, a multitude of instruments, and above all, one score adjusted to the tone capacity of each particular instrument. The whole orchestra is, in turn, in the hands of the conductor, who is responsible for the final harmonised result. I think it is a good analogy for our subject. In economic life we expected that a crowd of steelmakers, grain-producers, stockbrokers, engineers, who labour for profit's sake would produce an harmonious economy, in which the interests of the individual would be smoothly and naturally intertwined with the interests of the whole? Is then the self-interest of millions of individuals to be blamed for not producing automatically the desired harmony? And in most cases, conductors have been placed in charge, who not only pocket the fruits of their orchestra's labour, but also leave the harmony to take care of itself.

'In the case of our collective communities in Palestine – and now we return at last to our starting point – a single and reasonable economic system underlies and determines social relations. Our system confers on the individual such obvious benefits that he has come to regard the interests of the community as pre-conditional to his own welfare. That is my explanation of the survival of our way of life in this world of rapacious competitive selfishness. Once the "making of money" lost its hold over us as individuals, work and labour in field and factory, at the desk or at the easel, in the nursery, in school, in fact, all manual and intellectual work became again an act of creation and of self-expression.'

Our first heated discussion came to an end at this point. And although I remained adamant to the end on the general issues involved, I had had eventually to concede Reuben his point concerning the bonds which keep alive the collective settlement. I had to admit that such communities under the very adverse social and economic conditions of Palestine would not be in a position to preserve the allegiance of their adherents and their offspring on purely idealistic grounds, were they at variance with their own self-interests. Reuben's argument became even more convincing when I came to know his personal experience as a member of such a community.

CHAPTER TWO

MAN'S DESTINY

'CRISIS SCREAMED AT me at every turn, in that first year of perplexed gropings in Palestine. Physical collapse alternating with dumb despair served to bring me to the very edge of catastrophe.'

These were Reuben's opening sentences when we continued our story on Christmas Eve, 1944. The curfew for that night had been lifted by the German camp authorities, and for the first time in a year we walked again under a full moon, on a clear starry night. A sharp frost had covered the trees with a white crystalline layer, and the barbed wire of the perimeter in its new coat of heavy fuzzy bristles looked more solid and impenetrable than ever. The hard trodden snow under our feet creaked and grated sympathetically with our own desolate mood. For Reuben and myself it was the fourth Christmas within barbed wire, and the fifth away from home: for our friends captured in France it was the fifth Christmas in their P.O.W. career. The difference between former Christmas celebrations in captivity and the present one was sharply marked. It was no use pretending – we felt deeply disappointed, and cheated; although we had been aware of the moral and military reserves of the Germans – probably more so than the people at home, we had refused to entertain any doubts of their final overthrow before the year was out. But the leaves had fallen from the trees. Arnhem was gallantly fought and lost and progress all along the German frontiers slowed down. Still we clung to the hope that a major allied offensive would eventually pierce the German line in the West simultaneously with the Russian onslaught on the Eastern borders of the Reich. Both offensives came – at least that is how we termed the late autumn campaigns in the West and on the East Prussian border – and it became evident that the Germans now under Butcher Himmler's supreme dictatorship, had recovered sufficiently to be able to prolong the senseless and sacrificial struggle. And then nine days before Christmas, the greatest surprise of all was sprung on us by the German counter-offensive. To be frank no other reverse in the Allied fortunes during the five years of war had hurt us so deeply as this last one. I may safely say that for the first time in my P.O.W. experience I saw our people with their heads down; it was not despair because we knew enough of the situation to see that particular German effort in its proper perspective. It was something deeper and more wounding – it was a feeling akin to humiliation for having been made the victims of a bad joke. The precarious balance, a synthesis of inner resignation and of simmering optimism, from which a long-term P.O.W. draws his strength and sanity was violently upset. We had in all probability only ourselves to blame for it; nevertheless the chilling grip of a crisis was felt by every one of us. There was no display of emotion but there was also no attempt at festivity and cheerfulness, which in former days distinguished our Christmas days from the every day routine.

So when I came to keep my appointment with Reuben on that Christmas Eve I felt in tune with his recollections of the great crisis of his life which threatened to reduce to ashes the dreamland castles of his youth. In its way the story bears the familiar touches of many a pioneer life. The climate did not agree with him, the poor and meagre diet of a community crucified by unemployment, wrecked his none too vigorous constitution; diseases and epidemics originating from under-nourishment and from the unsanitary conditions of the Arab quarter where their camp was situated, found him an easy prey. Economic want, disillusionment, isolation from the rest of the Jewish world by the ban on immigration, all united to make a bid for the souls of the young, ecstatic immigrants. Reuben endowed with authority by virtue of his former leading position in the movement, himself assailed by a host of tempting devils, was expected by his comrades to show a way, when friends of older standing in the country appeared to lose their hold. It was all so confusing and exacting, and all he wanted was to be left alone in his physical and intellectual misery. He felt his vitality ebbing away, leaving him often quite unconscious of his surroundings. It was naturally not easy to make him talk of that period.

'I try hard', he assured me, 'to recollect what, and how, I felt in that first year of my Palestinian experience. But such things have a way of slipping out of mind. There is nothing tangible, and only the dimmest impression remains. Most of that year, I realise now, I must have spent in dumbness and silence, whimpering to myself like a wounded animal. Such phases in a pioneer life are normally exaggerated into a sort of heroism, or on the other hand are carefully obliterated for propaganda reasons, but the man who went through it had nothing to do with either of these considerations. I think I was hardly conscious of what was happening to me. There was no steady work to get used to. One day I hacked away for ten hours with a pick and shovel digging a narrow sewage ditch six feet deep, while the sun was beating on my bare shoulders and my shirt became so soaked in sweat that I had to discard it. The dust and the stench of the Arab quarter choked my lungs while the soft skin on the palms of my hands turned into a bloody pulp. The following day no more pick and shovel for me. I remained in camp where work was always plentiful; it was my turn to scrub the floors, tables, carry water from the well and to look after other household jobs. Such work did nothing to harden my hands since they were soaking in washtubs all day.

'Then might come a day's work on the scaffold of a building, and the wet cement would burn holes in toes and fingers. Adequate protective gloves or rubber boots were then for us unobtainable luxuries. After such a round of miscellaneous work my body would surrender to the exertions put upon it, I would suddenly find myself with a temperature of 105°, be it from popataccia, an acclimatisation fever, whose carrier is a sand fly; or be it malaria, typhoid, dysentery, or jaundice, all of which came my way in quick succession. After every bout of sickness, invariably accompanied in that blessed country with very high temperatures, I was reduced to a tottering skeleton which had to be nursed back to a human shape by the untiring devotion of the nurse, and in fact of the whole community. If starvation level was the rule for the healthy – the sick and infirm were never allowed to lack wholesome food, and indeed even little appetising luxuries often made an appearance on their menu.

'One felt, naturally, the urge to go back to work as quickly as possible, and then I made myself look fit and well in order to spare the community the heavy expenses which sickness incurred. So after one particular illness and some prevarications with doctor and nurses, I managed to get myself included in a detachment which was sent off to the Yezreel valley for irrigation work. There it was that, after a month of wading knee-deep in the mire and drinking the brackish water of the Arab ground-well, I went down with a severe attack of dysentry followed by jaundice. I had to spend a fortnight in a Government hospital. It was then, when asked by the clerk of the hospital for my name, that I remembered my illegal status: I knew that the immigration officers had me on their list of "illegals", since they well knew that any pioneer refused entry to the country would sooner or later find a way to slip in. I gave the clerk the Hebrew version of my family name, under which I eventually became naturalised. Government hospitals at that time were very primitive, and one dodged their shelter if possible, but there were no alternative institutions. We possessed as yet only few hospitals of our own, and none in the area in which I lived. As the disease was contagious I had to submit to detention in the Government hospital. I suppose the pious Arab nuns did their duty to the best of their ability, but the sick man became even sicker when presented with a bowl of revolting gruel and a cup of weak tea for each and every meal.'

Our conversation, or more precisely, Reuben's monologue, was here interrupted as we came up with the carol singers serenading in front of the camp's hospital for the benefit of the sick and wounded. It was a biggish choir of about 50 voices, singing with gusto the traditional carols, this particular one finishing with the clarion call:

Noël Noël Noël
Born is the King of Israel.

Reuben's thoughts must have wandered from our theme – for he came to with a start when I asked him to proceed with his story.

'It is just as well that the "King of Israel" has checked my trivial personal account.' Reuben turned to me apologetically while re-adjusting his balaclava and scarf. 'There is, however, one thing I should like you to mark; I am quite convinced that without the help of my community I would have perished in some garret or lean-to shed, the fate of many an individualistic pioneer. As most of us European immigrants went through similar stages of physical collapse, and as at that time – it improved out of recognition in the latter years – we still lacked adequate means for dealing with such contingencies, the collective group had to fulfil all the tasks of the social welfare institutions which we lacked. By mutual help we nursed ourselves back to health, putting aside for that purpose our scant earnings for the supply of the most urgent needs of the infirm. That arrangement saved us from the humiliating effects of charitable institutions, and cemented the bonds of friendship between us, as well as giving us our social independence from the cold outsider. This is one instance of what I meant when I tried to convey to your doubting mind that collectivism with us rested on a firmer foundation than idealism – it was, in fact, the answer to the self-interest of the pioneer in Palestine. The pioneering stage of a career there is infinitely longer than that of a pioneer in your part of the world. It certainly lasts the lifetime of the pioneer himself, and even stretches out well into the lifetime of his children. In one way or another I feel pretty certain that, had the pioneering spirit and effort with its manifold superstructures, both social and moral, not continued to permeate our work in Palestine, we might easily have become infested with the ideas of the Levant. Oriental stagnation and bigotry form a rich and lethal breeding ground in which new ideas and actions swiftly find their graves.

'The memories of the emotional and intellectual crisis of that year still evoke in me vivid and painful flashes of recollection. One is naturally very anxious to analyse the underlying factors of the crisis. Look at it perhaps this way. Our lovingly tended flower-garden sprouting with colourful ideas about the renaissance of our people was seen to wither under the scorching rays of a relentless reality. Although we – the new immigrants and young collectives – found ourselves part of an efficient and brave Federation of Jewish Labour in Palestine, which comprised at that time about ninety per cent. of all labourers, farmers and intellectual workers in the country who lived on their own toil, and although we had the benefit of their guidance and experience, we felt lonely and abandoned to our fate. Our youthful and enthusiastic spirits faltered and wavered, when confronted with the perplexing conditions of an undertaking riven by antagonism and stagnation.

'For one thing the meeting with the Mandatory administration of the country – British in the upper, and Arabic in the lower ranks of the hierarchy – was a chilling experience. With the exception of Field Marshal Plumer, then High Commissioner, who showed himself a humane and an objectively sympathetic administrator, all Government departments and officials turned to us a cold and often hostile shoulder. Their original distrust of the quaint Zionist enterprise appeared to be vindicated by the economic crisis which had arisen. They believed that they had done their share in the solution of the problem, by stopping immigration altogether. Our deepest resentment, however, was reserved for the Jewish people all over the world, who, as we then saw it, cared as little about our endeavour, as a Bantu for the salvation of his soul. The few thousand unemployed asked for nothing more than to be given the means to drain marshes, to build roads and houses, to irrigate and settle the waste and pestilential land which was there for the taking.

We argued about the question with our tongues still swollen from fever, and became convinced that it was not in the realm of possibility to hope that those people against whose ideas we had revolted would now come to our assistance. These Jews, we argued, wished only to be left alone, luxuriating in the fleshpots of Egypt; our faith in the possibility, and in the crying necessity of a Jewish renaissance, national and social, before disaster overtook their blinded selves, was but a chimera.

'Why and to what end were we throwing away our lives and careers for a seemingly hopeless undertaking? When we looked around us we paid little attention to the generation of pioneers which had preceded us, and come out victorious, firmly rooted in the soil of the country which they had revived. In a masochistic way we preferred to magnify *ad absurdum* the significance of the cynical orange plantation owners – pioneers who in their time had embraced the same lofty ideals as ourselves – and whom we now saw lording it over their Arab labourers – women and children among them; yet denying to us, their kin and followers, a day's work for the sake of the extra shilling or two which they made by employing the Arab half-nomad. Were we not – we asked ourselves – justified, nay morally obliged, to hurl the stone tablets of the new covenant at these people and their idolatry?

'You can see for yourself now, the crisis reached down to the very foundations of our existence. A battle royal developed in our community as in many another. While the large majority suffered the agony of their confused feelings, and battled against the surrender of their faith to the transitory grumbling of their stomachs, a few of our number eventually uttered a curse on their country and people, and proposed to put to the test the alternative salvation: Soviet Russia.

'You are surprised? You see the men and women who raised that banner thought that by turning to Russia they would camouflage the all too obvious reasons for their desertion; they held that they merely exchanged one revolutionary ideal for another. The first ideal to which they had subscribed had failed because of the crisis in the country for which, they asserted complacently, British imperialistic policy was responsible. The second ideal – the new world of Soviet Russia – had proved itself a success – and success was for them the indisputable criterion for the feasibility of their ideals.

'There were but a handful who took the plunge and left the country and our cause. They went to serve a movement which, although of world-stirring importance, had failed to provide a constructive answer to the national complexity of Jewry. I have learned since that they fared badly in the country of their adoption, all of them in fact finished in Siberia, but that is another story. The mass of our people were not so easily shaken, and the struggle with our own weaknesses went on.'

Our time was up and the long walk in the sharp air had fairly exhausted the meagre number of calories which the German diet, and half a Red Cross parcel a week, supplied us with. I have had to rely on further talks at odd intervals to complete the picture. The ideological crisis I learned was eventually overcome, as was the economic depression. It was conquered by sheer doggedness of purpose, by the faith characteristic of the new Jewish proletariat, and not least by the quality of the Labour leadership. Nevertheless, Reuben asserts, the vicissitudes of the economic and ideological struggle have left their mark still discernible in some quarters of Palestine Labour. The sour taste of the experience has faded, but one may still come up against its subconscious workings. To those who have recovered from their disillusionment – although they refused to desert the cause, and to flee the country – a touch of cynical abandon serves as a substitute for their former enthusiasm. Some went further and under cover of a 'Weltanschauung' became violently anti-Zionist and anti-British, on occasions they did not even shrink from provoking Arab brigands to attack and burn Jewish settlements. The perversity of such an aberration struck me as something unprecedented in the field of psychological experience. How came it to be? A temporary economic depression, unemployment and even a feeling of having been betrayed by one's own people could scarcely have brought about such destructive reactions?

'For my generation, solidarity of the individual Jew with Jewry as a nation was a wilful act of the intellect', Reuben stated in answer to my enquiry. 'We had to overcome much (remember the convention I told you about), to win through to an active Jewish conscience; there was as yet no Hitler to decide the matter for us. In times of crisis, such as we went through, a new searching of heart brought the problem again to the fore, settled it and confirmed our allegiance to our people as an inescapable historical fact; leaving us fully determined to bear the consequences of our convictions. But there were amongst us some deeply involved in cosmopolitan escapism, who had never struck root in any country. Of them one might well say: "Ubi bene, ibi patria". On the other hand any crisis was enough to send them packing, to explore new fields. As to the perversity of inciting gangs of rioters against their own blood – I am afraid we are not the only people who have perpetrated such monstrosities. Admittedly it is easier for such types to breed in an atmosphere of national decay than amidst a firmly rooted national life; nevertheless, every nation has had to contend, in times of crisis, with individuals who sympathised with the enemy, or even brought themselves to act treacherously. There is always an ideology at hand to cloak such acts, and to represent them to the world as high principled martyrdom and self-negation. Essentially it is lack of character. I have been present at the birth and baptism of such ideologies, and I know them for what they are: the impact of crisis and disillusionment on weak ill-formed characters; a pitiful personal tragedy for the victims of such illusions. Unhappily they have a way of making others pay the price for their weakness, but in the end, however, even diluted blood ties prove themselves stronger than a denationalised cosmopolitan ideology.'

Reuben himself, saddled with the responsibilities of his community, emerged from the crisis relieved of many illusions, but the richer for an experience which deepened his sense of practical values. The manifold physical sufferings had, however, bred 'that most obnoxious of human weaknesses, self-pity', which had to be overcome before recovery began.

The ruthless analysis of the crisis as applied by them had brought the community back to a balanced appreciation of its position; the social atmosphere cleared, and recovery was swift. Reuben has no clear recollection of how he himself climbed out of the slough of despondency. It had much to do with the fact of his physical recovery, as he steadily became immune to the prevailing scourges of the country. When he found himself putting on flesh again, and the haze which had enveloped him being dispersed by his growing vitality – he could scarcely believe that there was anything wrong with the world, or with that particular fragment of it which was his by destiny and adoption.

Quite unexpectedly, he found himself one evening talking to

the assembled community. His friends – so Reuben assured me – did not quite know what to make of that speech – neither did Reuben for that matter: nevertheless his words had a deep effect on their minds and feelings. Drawing my own conclusions, I would say that his speech had that quixotic freshness which so often gives relief to people enmeshed in an inhibitive tangle. After months of maddening arguments, outbursts of self-pity and of sadistic self-purgings – there fell suddenly on their ears the scratching of an old record – which had long since been forgotten. Thoughts and feelings began to sort themselves out: they heard that all their sufferings had been the birth pangs of that movement to which they had dedicated themselves when breaking with their old environments: they came back to that old truth that a revolutionary cannot hope to be patted on the back by the world which he has defied; that such an endeavour as Zionism was not a pleasure walk with a band playing music in front; and I gather there was much more on these lines in Reuben's outburst. We may picture to ourselves a Reuben with his cheeks aglow, but with eyes still protruding from his drawn face, conveying to his friends a new enthusiasm. It was, they realised, the illness of the spirit which must first be combated. That evening, after a long interval, the mouth-organs were taken out again and in ecstatic folk-dances they gave vent to the feeling that the tide had turned.

Then one evening Reuben's eyes lighted again on Chick, who was hovering on the fringes of the whirling circle. Later on the same evening he led her out for a stroll on the beach. She said 'yes' when he proposed. When both of them returned to the dining hall the crowd was already dispersing, but Deb, who had a passion for romance, was quick to read the signs in Reuben's and Chick's radiant faces. It was the signal for a new round of jigs. At the same time Sarah, the keeper of the store-room keys, was ransacking the pantry, and produced trays of sandwiches with nothing in between, and oranges, for it was the season of the orange harvest and they were 20 to a penny. Reuben and Chick were married six months later, and Reuben brought his wife, already well known to the community, to live with him in a tent. That tent was to be their home for many years, until they moved into a wooden hut, and finally, in their own agricultural settlement – to a stone and concrete house. The lifting of the depression opened the way for many marriages, and sharp on time the cry of babies came to replace the whimperings of disillusionment.

M

CHAPTER THREE

ONE AND ONE MAKE THREE

IT WOULD BE deceptive to assume that Reuben's community could have recovered its equilibrium by a mere spiritual effort. The interplay between the economy and the state of mind of a society is so subtly woven that we often miss the causality between them. The fact that week by week more members of the community found themselves continuously employed; that the purse of the treasurer, and with it the woodstores, began to swell; and that the sick list went down, contributed decisively to the change of feelings.

On the other hand a closer study reveals that the economic change was entirely wrought by an effort of the will. The determination of the Zionist and Labour leaders which had lent confidence to dormant private initiative, became in the end economic factors of the first order. When Reuben's first year of initiation was over, the throb of constructive work and of new settlement was heard again in town and country. With unemployment defeated, the clamour for the re-opening of immigration – which was maintained even during the years of depression – rose to a pitch. The Government, bound by the Mandate to facilitate Jewish immigration had to rescind its policy in the light of the economic changes which had taken place. Since the improvement was judged to be of a sound and durable nature, an immigration schedule for six months was devised. With the arrival of the new and vigorous waves of immigrants, including pioneers, middle classes and capitalists (estimated at one thousand pounds and above) economic activity widened over many new fields, and with it began one of the most prosperous eras in the development of the country.

Except for a slight downward curve during the riots of 1929 known as the 'wailing wall incident' prosperity continued unbroken until the Arab rebellion in 1936, and beyond it. In those eight or nine years, both the Jewish and the Arab sectors of the country developed so strongly as to change the very character of the Palestinian landscape. To mention only a few of the many marks of constructive growth which Reuben witnessed during those years: the Jewish population almost doubled its size, approaching the half million mark; the first deep water harbour of the country was begun and finished; Haifa Bay, the remainder of the Armaggedon and Kishon valleys, as well as the Sharon plain, were cleared of swamp and malaria and opened up to new colonization; the Palestine Electric Company began and finished its first Hydro-power plant where the Jarmuk joins the Jordan; Haifa, Tel Aviv and Jaffa saw the first sizeable industrial plants completed; rising water towers signalled the foundation of more and more agricultural settlements; and in the Arab villages new stretches of orchards, well irrigated land and new modern agricultural implements were to be noticed. Over a million trees were planted. Reuben's eyes gleamed when he recounted for my benefit, work on work, and achievement on achievement. The years of crippling crisis, of anguish and despair lived on in memory as a bad dream, but they eventually became obliterated by the passion for creative work which at last found an outlet.

Reuben remembered clearly that Labour conference, a milestone in the history of modern Palestine, at which over five hundred delegates and thousands of guests, the latter in the main unemployed, had met with the aim of 'breaking the neck of idleness and waste'. For this was the slogan under which the conference worked. It was, as might be expected, an uproarious meeting; floor and gallery took a passionate stand on the problems at issue, and the chairman and his bell worked frantically to curb excessively passionate and idle oratory. That conference marked the opening of the new phase of prosperity. Reuben called it the 'historical conference'.

'I went to the conference as one of the delegates from Haifa.' I quote for accuracy's sake Reuben's own words. 'We were heartily sick of two or three days' work a week at the best. The discussions as to how to liquidate the "crisis" – the cryptic name given to the general conditions of the country and our own people – had come to an end, and of all the schemes suggested there remained one alone which fired the imagination and hopes of Labour. That scheme consisted of a general offensive against unemployment, in all sectors of the Jewish economic life. All available public funds, bank credits, government grants, and private initiative were to be combined to feed this most ambitious, and yet practical, scheme. 'Elementary mathematical economy, which insists that one plus one makes always two and no more, was to be discarded for the sake "of a higher mathematical order", by which one plus one makes three. This could be done by the introduction of a new mathematical symbol, by name, "Faith", as the chief promoters of the scheme put it. I was then a humble spectator on the floor of the house, as it was practically my first contact with a representative assembly of Labour in Palestine. The conference was held in a bare ugly hall, the Tel Aviv Exhibition premises. The deliberations lasted for five days and nights and I think that there was never a slack moment in its proceedings. Labour party leaders, Trade Union officials, collective and co-operative farmers, plantation labourers and old gnarled pioneers jostled in the crowd, together with recently smuggled-in immigrants, mixing on tiptoe with old and tired-looking pioneer women, the labour of a life-time mirrored in the wrinkles of their benevolent faces. Young pioneer girls from the town collectives, their red handkerchiefs slipping coquettishly from their dark locks, were to be seen side by side with small dark Yemenite delegates in half-oriental attire, with their curly side locks swinging excitedly whenever they moved or talked. There was also a number of stately Arab delegates, representing the first International Union of the country – the Railway – and Post employees – who added lustre to the drama which was being played with tremendous vitality and vigour. Besides the array of the leaders of the Labour movement, two men in particular held sway over the meeting; they were the authors of the scheme which was presented to the assembly by the Executive council of the Labour Federation.

There were striking differences between these two – both in their outward appearance as well as in their personalities. They shared, however, one outstanding characteristic: a fanatical conviction that the so-called objective economic or political conditions could, and should, be ironed out by the will-power of men of faith. This view was opposed by a considerable section of the assembly which clung stubbornly to the idea that such problems as the assembly was called on to deal with could not be solved without the initiative, and means, of the Government. And since the Palestine Government was in alien and indifferent hands, they proclaimed that the only thing Labour should do was to apply political pressure, by means of direct action of the unemployed. Against that political bias, both DAN and JOSEF insisted on the self-action of the Labour and Zionist movements, in addition to any help which might be gained from the Palestine Administration. The two of them with the support of the political and Union Leaders eventually carried the conference by an overwhelming majority.'

'Before you proceed any further', I interrupted, 'I should like to know something more substantial about these two men whose names you have just mentioned. You see, Reuben, I learn more through acquaintance with the characters acting in the drama of life, than by measuring the pits filled with the dry bones of theory and ideas.'

'You old fox, Jack, you cannot deceive me', Reuben had found me out in a flash. 'You still have your mind on your book. Here am I, talking myself hoarse, and what do I get for it – dry bones – indeed! All you seem to be interested in is the description of exotic characters among whom you probably class my friends and myself. I feel that I am turning myself inside out to convey to you the ideas, ideas man, it is they that matter. You insist? As you wish – I do not mind in the least, after so many years of separation, picturing myself again in the company of my dear friends.

'I have mentioned Dan – well, to give him his full name Dan Kornblum came to Palestine at the beginning of the century as a myopic, but stocky young man. He belonged to a generation which had spent its youth in rabbinical colleges, training for future religious leadership of the Jewish communities, spread as they were all over the domains of the Czarist Empire. But tightly shut windows and jealous prefects were quite unable to avert the modernistic draughts from blowing in on the young students. In fact the modern trends in politics and literature, all classed summarily under the title "revolutionary", became, as time went on, of more interest to the pupils than the bulky tracts of the Talmud. Tolstoi, Kropotkin, and Marx came to be read stealthily during unnaturally prolonged sessions in the college latrines, or tucked away under bed-covers. One kind of literature, negligently handled by the Czarist censors and secret police, but far more fiercely indicted by the college authorities, was the Zionist literature. Such pamphlets were on the index, and any pupil found in possession of such radical heresy was certain of a flogging, followed up by extra exercises in mediæval scholastic treatises. Dan, like many of his colleagues, considering such a routine irksome and unpalatable for their newly conceived ideas, solved the difficulty by running away from the Seminaries and embarking for Palestine. A few went with the blessings of their parents, but more went without. Young Dan, we may be sure, had the shock of his life when he took his first look at the Holy Land, and realised to what state the Old Turk and the Arabs between them had reduced the place. It was the year 1906 A.D. The Jewish plantations had little use for the young scholarly undergraduates, but the latter, by agreeing to work under the same conditions as the Arab labourers, succeeded eventually in getting employment. We can see bespectacled Dan, his fighting chin sticking out, and his robust body rising to its full five feet five inches, as he challenged his Arab mate to a hoeing race along the narrow and overgrown alley in between the citrus trees. More often than not he would lose the race, his Arab competitor either jeering at the feeble Muscovite or, just possibly, generously praising the pluck of the defeated "Hawaja". But when young Dan happened to win, his fame would spread all over the colony. In the evening Dan's achievement would be the main topic of discussion among the small group of Jewish labourers.

'The cabin in which Dan and three of his comrades lived, served also as a meeting place, for Dan had been elected to be the first secretary of the Association of Agricultural Labourers. A plain wooden bunk served him as a desk, and when the meagre oil supply in his lamp gave out, he would lie down on it to rest his fatigued body and brain. At the crack of dawn he would be up, grasp his hoe and off to the village square, where overseers, lounging astride their sleek donkeys, were hiring farm hands for the day.

'One day a pioneer, clad in rags, and covered in dust from a hundred odd miles' march down from Galilee, brought sensational news from the North. It appeared that the few scattered Jewish colonies in the North, founded by a pious Rothschild philanthropist, were paying forced tributes to nomadic chieftains for the sake of shielding the colonies from robberies and attacks by their Arab neighbours. Quick-silver Dan flew into one of his phenomenal rages, climbed on to a stool and ordered a meeting to consider the steps to be taken to put a stop to such a degrading subservience by the Northern Colonists. He rushed to the hut, and striking a pin against a cast iron pipe suspended from a wire, he gave the popular signal for an urgent meeting. The colony was small and the community of the Jewish pioneers still smaller. Every one of them on hearing the dull strokes rushed instantly to Dan's cabin. There was the "boss", clad in a sweaty shirt with sleeves rolled up to his elbows, revealing brown muscular fore-arms, his stumpy legs clad in greasy cotton trousers, and feet shod with nondescript gaping footgear, ready to harangue the assembly. He never lacked a plan of action, even in those early days of his career. He moved then and there to organise "the Order of the Knight Pioneer" for the protection of the northern colonies. Dan had heard of many such isolated attempts in the past, which although heroically undertaken, had failed because the colonists were timid, and the knights too small in numbers for the task. His motion was seconded and approved on the spot.

'The next morning an early riser would have met Dan as he, with ten or fifteen followers were setting out for their crusading march to Galilee; on their way they broadcast their appeal from colony to colony, and when Kornblum finally reached the Galilee colonies many pioneers had swelled the numbers of the knights. They scattered over the colonies, lived and slept in stables and haybarns, worked when work was to be obtained and in the evenings and on Sabbath days they met and argued about organi-sation and the election of committees; the buying of shot-guns and mares, and tactics to be employed to win over the colonists for their plans of self defence. The colonists were not easily per-suaded. They argued with their would-be protectors that the nomadic chieftains would burn their colonies and massacre their families if they antagonised them by discontinuing their tribute.

'The Knights decided then, on Dan's suggestion, to take the protection of the colonies into their own hands. The rivalry preva-lent amongst the nomadic chieftains for the tribute of the colonists was fought out at the expense of the colonies. Repeated thefts and destruction of property were committed by the rivals of the chieftains receiving tribute, to remind the colonies that they had chosen impotent weaklings for their protectors. Such vile manœuvres played into the hands of the Knights Pioneer and they were not slow in grasping the opportunity. Dan and his crowd decided to strike at the root of the trouble by treating the "protectors" and their rivals in the same way. The colonists soon realised that true protection of their property and lives, and salvation from the indignity of tribute, were only possible by co-operating with the Order of the Knights. Many a brave lad lost his life in that struggle, but the Knights, now staunchly assisted by the encouraged colonists, prevailed in the end. The payment of tribute ceased and with it peace came to the colonies.

'The cessation of the tribute had definitely improved the relations between the Jewish colonies and their nomadic neighbours. Having accomplished that, Dan turned to the organisation of the first National Federation of the Agricultural Labourers in Palestine.

'While Dan was busy in Galilee, a group of agricultural labourers, distinguished by their constructive rather than political turn of mind, had laid the foundation of the first collective community – the mother of all communal settlements in the country. That collective community – which built the first settlement of its kind at the point where the Jordan flows out from the lake of Galilee – was not the creation of an idealistic whim but was developed steadily, over a period of years, from lower grades of co-operation between the pioneers and their families until it reached the form of a fully developed communal society.

'Dan Kornblum liked the idea, and followed the lead by organising the second collective. That Jack, is how, 1,900 years after the Sermon on the Mountain, Galilee again became the scene for the birth of a new social order.

'Dan, however, was not allowed to settle down and rest on his laurels. He had grown into a national personality. Take a glimpse at him again. He has aged, grey streaks prematurely invade his dark chestnut mop of hair which is still in dire need of trimming; down covers his elongated upper-lip; there is no break in his nomadic peregrinations. It is to be noticed that having become a member of a well-cared-for community he is now more neatly, if not exactly elegantly dressed, and on the whole he appears to us almost civilized. It is the year 1913. He bears the proud title of Secretary of the Agricultural Labour Federation, fully-equipped – the rumour has it – with an office, a desk, and a bunk to sleep in. His office is established in Jerusalem. But there are few people who could testify that they have ever managed to find him in his office. With a satchel on his back, in which a towel and even a tooth-brush, but above all a bunch of papers and note-books are stowed away, Dan journeys all over the country. Meetings with workers and their committees; frantic quarrels with employers for wages and work; haggling with Arabs for a plot of land or bribing Turkish officials for a permit to erect a stable, which in the end turned out to be a large colony; all these and many other cares are among his self-imposed tasks. People of all classes of the population, including Arab effendis and minor Turkish officials may spend days in seeking Dan Kornblum. He himself has never failed in finding a man he wants. If he has had to drag him out of his bed at dawn, he would be there in order not to miss him. Which reminds me, that when I had business with him – about fifteen years ago – he fixed the appointment for six o'clock in the morning in his office if, as he said, I wished to have a productive and undisturbed talk with him. Productive the talk turned out to be, but undisturbed by no means, because I had not been the only client invited for a "productive and undisturbed" hour.

'I see, you are getting restive. I'll cut the story short. When the war broke out in 1914, with Turkey in due course joining the Central powers, Palestine Jewry became subjected to the most atrocious persecutions. Everything the Turks, and eventually their German allies, could lay hands on was confiscated; hundreds and thousands of Jews were driven into exile and a number of them thrown into jail for conspiring with the Allies. Dan Kornblum became in those times of stress the father of the Jewish working communities. He organised food supplies and distribution, saved thousands from famine by calling in American Relief, freed prisoners from jail, and so forth, but these activities came suddenly to a standstill, when Dan with five other representative men of Palestine Jewry, was arrested and marched off in chains to Damascus. They were charged with high treason and condemned to death. By the intervention of foreign consuls and by other agencies their sentence was commuted to imprisonment for life.

'Dan, after many hair-raising adventures, managed to escape and to reach Alexandria where he immediately joined up with the Zion Rifles. No sooner was Palestine liberated than Dan, still wearing his sloppy army uniform, was to be seen preparing for the reconstruction work by buying up old army barracks, machinery, and other equipment. Nobody – including his C.O., I suppose, ever knew exactly whether or not at that time he was still in the army – where he attained the high rank of Lance-corporal, or whether he had been demobbed. When things settled down under the post-war Mandatory establishment, Dan Kornblum became the head and leader of the swiftly expanding Jewish colonization of the country.

'Well, that is the life sketch of the man whom I saw now in the centre of the proceedings of the Labour conference. He had changed profoundly. If anything his glasses had thicker lenses, his still abundant hair was a sheet of silver, his suit was clean, and

the shirt, open at the neck, spotlessly white – but the same un-
curbed vitality and untiring devotion to the cause still animated
his whole being.

'What did he have to say on that occasion? It would lead us too
far to deal with his scheme to "wipe out the dastardly shame of
unemployment from the face of Eretz Israel". He had one argument which he drove home ruthlessly, I thought it then quite
unanswerable in its elementary human appeal. The word "I" you
should note, stood in Dan's highly original vocabulary for the
organisation he represented.

' "I have at my disposal,," he cried, "25,000 acres of land.
There is plenty of water above and below it. I have thousands of
candidates, well-trained, hard-working, intelligent boys and
lovely girls, who are willing and capable of bringing that land
back to life and fruitfulness. I have hundreds of families already
settled on the land, but they still live in tents and tumbledown
corrugated iron shacks. They need urgently houses of stone and
concrete, and I have stone quarries next door to their homes. I
have two dozen settlements whose agricultural products are
ruined before they reach the consumer for lack of decent roads.
I have work, crying, urgent work for thousands of people. I want
'a few' thousand pounds, and the money is there in the pockets
and safes of our compatriots. It is a libel if anybody maintains
that the Jews are unwilling to help us, and themselves. We can
have the money, whether as donation or as a loan is immaterial
– but we do not know how to ask for it. I shall go myself, and
take with me some men and women from this assembly, and I
swear we shall not be sent back empty handed by our brothers
and sisters abroad." This is just a sample of his talk.

'Yes, he went abroad with a mission, and was as good as his
word. There you are, Jack, I hope I have satisfied your curiosity.
That is Dan Kornblum, at present the Head of the Federation of
Agricultural Workers, which includes the settlers on the land
owned by the nation, as well as hired farm and plantation hands.
He now has an office with several clerks, and the organisation owns
many fine buildings and co-op plants for the utilisation of agricultural products. He does not sleep any longer on the desk at his
office, but, to enjoy a "productive and undisturbed" talk with him
one is still well-advised to meet him at 6 o'clock in the morning,
or to corner him in one of the taxi-buses plying between Tel Aviv
his H.Q., and Jerusalem, the seat of the Jewish Agency.'

When I had asked Reuben to give me a sketch of the two
personalities who focussed the attention of the conference on
themselves, I had not foreseen that I would be given the opportunity of catching an inside view of the life and doings of the
forerunners of Reuben's own pioneer generation. The sketch on
Dan Kornblum followed up by the story of Josef Lubin, who
belonged to the early post-war immigration wave, has supplied
the missing link up to Reuben's own time. For Josef Lubin represented yet another type of that heterogeneous nucleus which went
to the making of Palestine pioneerdom.

'Josef Lubin, the head of the Labour Centre for Planning,
which deals chiefly with the blue-printing of immigration and
employment schemes, represents the younger type of Labour
leader', Reuben told me à propos of a review of Palestinian Labour
establishments. 'He came to Palestine with the immigration
wave which the Russian revolution precipitated at the end of the
last war. As a student of economics and politics at the rapidly
Bolshevised Charkov University, a promising career in revolutionary Russia, which had swept away all anti-Jewish disability
acts of Czarist days, was open to him. But the bloody scenes of
massacre perpetrated by White Ukrainian anti-revolutionary
bands against the Jewish mass centres in the Ukraine had left
their indelible marks on Lubin, the young member of a Jewish
self-defence organisation. He had an answer ready for the en-
chanting, if sincere, advances of the new Russia: "None of your
sting and none of your honey", he quoted to the gentile and
Jewish representatives of the new order, and lost no time in
joining the columns of young intellectuals who marched a thousand and more miles to reach Palestine.

'Young Josef stood six foot in his socks, a lanky and thin-
framed man. We may be sure that the breaking in of such a delicate physique to the hard work of road construction and stone-
quarrying was a painful experience for Lubin. In the early
twenties, however, those were the chief tasks which absorbed
the thousands of post-revolutionary pioneers who streamed into
Palestine. The construction of the modern metalled highways
from Haifa to Galilee, and from Haifa to Jerusalem, and the
quarrying of stone for their foundations was then in progress.
Lubin and his comrades, organised in big collective groups, had
pitched their tents along the chalky band of road, and each camp
became known by the milestone at which it was stationed. An

observer would have seen Josef Lubin by day kneeling on his knees laying the stone foundations for the highway, or sitting astride a pile of stones knocking away for dear life with his stone-breaker's hammer. When work was over he might be found in the office tent, looking after accounts or arranging the roster for the next day's work, or more often he might be stretched out on his belly behind a boulder on one of the hills overlooking the newly dug banks of the road, poring over a tattered old book. Malicious tongues will tell you that one day an overseer had found him when breaking up stones swinging his hammer to the rhythm of a poem by Pushkin whose book of songs lay open in front of him. Josef Lubin denies the story – as you would expect him to do – since he is now responsible for large-scale enterprises, and it would not do for any labourer to take it into his head to read Homer while paving a road.

Josef Lubin, however, very soon proved to his deriders that he was not a mere unpractical theorist. Some maintain that all that followed was purely Lubin's revenge on a contractor, hard as nails, who used to greet him every morning with "a good morning Pushkin." What happened was that Lubin conceived and propounded to his mates the idea that contractors were a parasitic nuisance, and that the two thousand odd labourers employed on the construction of highways could organise a co-operative contracting office and undertake and sign contracts under their own ægis. Men of Lubin's fibre have frequently to contend with the petty derision of their fellow men. He found now that his already familiar titles of professor and poet, were augmented by the address: "By His Majesty's appointment contractor." Josef Lubin remained unperturbed and was presumably too much absorbed in his calculations to take notice of the shafts aimed at him by the wiseacres. Self-consciousness was certainly an unknown entity to him. He bided his time, and proceeded with his preparations – in case an opening might present itself. It was not long in coming. One of the contractors suddenly stopped payments and announced to the world his condition of bankruptcy. Lubin was ready for the emergency, and his offer to take over the contract was accepted, though with little enthusiasm by the representatives of the Public Works department. The Contracting Office of the Labour Federation – to-day the biggest contracting firm in the Near East – was born on the day when Lubin signed the contract with the P.W.D. engineer. The experiment was a success. That job finished, and an extra bonus paid out to the labourers, Lubin went in search of new contracts. The tiny contracting department grew in a short time into a big co-operative firm employing thousands of labourers. A new type of management was now required endowed with a sense of money values and a knowledge of the handling of the credit and debit sides of the business. There was plenty of commercial talent to be found and Lubin, not feeling equal to such a task, was only too glad to accept the call of the Labour Federation to head the department for economic research and planning. He left the line of purely academic research and statistics to his collaborators, while he himself concentrated on the task of preparing the ground for new immigration. This he did by the promotion of vast public utility schemes, for which he not only planned, but also gained the support of the bodies concerned, to make them co-operate in the execution of his daring schemes.

'The same Josef Lubin', continued Reuben eagerly, 'I now saw in front of me at the Conference. With statistical columns at his elbow, fully prepared to meet criticism of one scheme by pushing forward an alternative, he stood on the platform in front of the seething audience, arguing against a radical delegate who attempted to prove scientifically and objectively that Labour itself could do nothing to ameliorate the cruel fate of the unemployed. Unemployment, the dogmatics maintained, was the responsibility of the capitalists and of the imperialistic administration of the country, and instead of dealing – as the innocent and rather naïve Lubin did – with constructive plans, they proposed that the conference should accept their plan of direct action. Josef Lubin who had not only columns of figures at his disposal, but also a rich fund of popular anecdotes and Jewish wit, abandoned his statistics and turned on his opponents with biting satire. He had probably come to the conclusion that by pure reasoning he would not succeed in combating the comfortable suggestions of the opposition who laid everything at the door of the Government and the "system" – so he treated the conference to one of his fables. I am ashamed to admit that of all the proceedings of this memorable conference, which started successfully the liquidation of the depression, at that time of vital personal interest to me, I remember best Lubin's fable of the two frogs. I am telling it to you privately, and God forbid you should disgrace your book with the story', admonished Reuben.

Notwithstanding the admonition – here is a rehash of the old fable.

'One frog, according to Lubin, was broad in the beam, slow to move, and by profession, a professor. The other was a skinny, but brawny, navvy frog. These two representatives of frogdom happened to meet on one of their nightly expeditions, inside a damp room in a farm dairy. They were attracted by a luminous white butter churn which on inspection proved to contain very appetising cream, ready set for the housewife's morning chore. Jumping on to the top of the butter churn, the professor lost his hold and fell into the creamy substance. The navvy frog attracted by the cries of his nocturnal acquaintance of high station, hurried to his rescue to find himself promptly dragged into the mess, by his weighty fellow sufferer. The position in which both frogs found themselves, we may imagine – was not cheerful – but the measures taken by the victims of their own greed were as completely different as were their stations in life. The professor after ascertaining by a quick and brilliant analysis that the substance of a frog was heavier than buttercream and that his chances to keep afloat were nil, resigned himself to the inviolable law of physics. He gave up his struggle, and sank slowly but surely to the bottom, to die an ignominious death by suffocation. The navvy frog, on the other hand, was a fellow quite ignorant of physical laws, but possessed of a strong desire to live. He reacted instinctively in a rather primitive way, by straining his muscular limbs to the utmost to keep afloat, thus shaking off the clammy substance and remaining on top of it. When morning dawned and the Farmer's wife approached the buttercream a most puzzling spectacle met her eyes. She found her work already done, obviously by the intervention of some mysterious agency.

'There before her, was a solid lump of butter, carrying on top of it an exhausted, bedraggled, but very much alive frog, while at the bottom of the churn veiled by the greasy liquid of the butter milk, lay another frog – broad and peaceful indeed, but stone dead.' 'Just a silly fable,' remarked Reuben, 'ancient and faded one would say, but still it was timely and to the point.'

'Josef Lubin', Reuben summed up his sketch, 'won his point – then and on several other occasions, as much by his shrewd wit as by his figures. For as I myself have learned to my cost, when my turn came to deal with large audiences it is seldom the force of convincing logical deductions, which wins for you their approval. More often it will be triviality, a sentiment or parallel unconsciously uttered which will carry the day for you. Both Kornblum and Lubin in the end won their point with the Conference. I cannot tell you, Jack, how the development which followed the Labour Conference, looked to those at the top – I only know how it looked to us, the unemployed of that time. To us it meant work and health. And it was good.'

That is the story of Dan and Josef as told by Reuben and recorded by me – the story of how one plus one plus 'Faith' make three.

CHAPTER FOUR

THE MAKING OF A SOCIETY

REUBEN, BACK FROM the momentous Conference, jumped straight into the whirl of hard, if exhilarating, menial jobs, which were now materialising with remarkable speed. The proud resolution of Labour to defeat unemployment had been given a warm welcome by all classes of the population. The Zionist authorities responded to the call, and together with the financial and economic corporation mobilised adequate funds. Large-scale public works, for which blue-prints lay ready at hand, were slowly and steadily getting under way.

Among the first schemes to be put into force was the draining of the Haifa Bay basin, a malaria-infested stretch of swamp and marsh. It was there that Reuben and his mates found employment. The wages paid on piece-work yielded an average of 8-10 shillings for an eight-hour day's work – which by Palestinian standards is considered to be a good wage. The work, under the scorching sun, ankle- and sometimes knee-deep in water, was hard, and the workers toiled like people obsessed, who were out to make up for the time of enforced idleness. No machines (except for the transport of the loam and sand) were used in order to augment the number of labourers employed. Only later, when unemployment was reduced to the minimum, were excavators put to work. Reuben and his mates were happy to see that the weekly cheques which their toil was bringing in for the community, allowed for a generous re-stocking of larder and stores.

When Ruthenberg, whose fame from his revolutionary exploits in Czarist Russia was now considerably enhanced by the renown which his constructive genius had earned for him in Palestine, began the erection of the first hydraulic power plant on the Jarmuk-Jordan juncture, a new field of work was opened. Ruthenberg made it his ambition to pay the best wages in the country and to get in exchange the sincerest effort and highest degree of craftsmanship from his employees. Hundreds and thousands of workers flocked to work for 'Ruthenberg', and he in turn chose from his engineers and labourers the managers and directors for his many-sided constructional activities in the country. Reuben's community seized the opportunity to dispatch a detachment of twenty men and women to work at 'Ruthenberg's' station. Then, with the boom returning to the building trade the community equipped its own Building Guild, and took on contracts for the erection of the reinforced concrete skeletons of the houses. With these and other jobs, all hands were fully employed and freshly-arrived pioneers from the mother movements abroad found themselves warmly welcomed. Within a few months Reuben's community doubled its membership to two hundred men and women, and the thoughts of everyone turned intently to the realisation of their main objective, settlement on the land.

New colonization, under Dan Kornblum's inspired leadership, had begun with the first blows which Labour and the Jewish Agency had delivered against unemployment, and there was a chance that Reuben's community might at last make a start with their agricultural settlement. The preparations for such an undertaking did not end with negotiations with the authorities in question; the Collective itself had to be brought in line for such a change. Men and women, outstanding in their agricultural training, and endowed with that intrinsic feeling for living things were sent to old and prosperous settlements, to acquire experience in the laying-out and management of all the details pertinent to mixed farming. A considerable part of the earnings of the community were put aside for the acquisition of such things as working beasts, carts, agricultural implements, timber and corrugated iron sheets. In order to strengthen their claim the community had to establish a detachment in a plantation colony – in close neighbourhood to the tract of land on the Sharon plain where new land was to be opened up for colonization; in the meantime the Collective body was split up into several detachments, so as to be close to the working-place and to provide means for the colonization effort. The additional task of keeping contact, adjusting living conditions, and of maintaining two and three camps, weighed heavily on the life of the community. The social conveniences, however, had to take second place when the economic and financial interests demanded it. Reuben's account of what colonization and settlement meant in Palestine made it plain that no parallels could be drawn between conditions in any of our Dominions and colonies and those prevailing in Palestine.

I myself have had a glimpse into one phase of Palestinian

colonization. It happened during the riotous years of 1936-39 and it certainly presented itself to me as one of the quaintest spectacles I had ever witnessed. The particular incident I am about to relate was, I assume, part and parcel of the Jewish strategy quite successfully employed during the three years of the riots. Throughout those troubled times the Jews had been making every conceivable effort to maintain intact the life and work of the country by pretending to ignore the Arab revolt altogether. Presumably they had it in mind to demonstrate to the Government and world opinion in general that the Jewish community in Palestine was already so firmly rooted as to be able to carry on the intricate machinery of communications, immigration, and colonization of land, as well as to look after the defence of their life and property against the well-organised Arab sabotage. Reuben at any rate asserts – and there is much to support his contention – that as far as the Jewish sector of life and economy was concerned – their policy was a complete success. However that may be, it is unquestionable that new colonization, on a fairly large scale for Palestinian conditions, was forced up during the years of trial and of one such example I became quite accidentally the amused spectator.

My unit happened to be stationed at the time in the South of Palestine with the task of securing the lines of communication and of lending assistance to the Police forces in case of major disturbances. There, on an early spring morning, my sleep was disturbed by the roar of trucks, the rattling of tractors, and the animated shouting of people. When I looked out of my bungalow, which was placed inconveniently close to the highway leading south to the Egyptian frontier, the advent of dawn was as yet only feebly indicated by a few streaks of grey and silver from the East and by the dim reflection of the morning haze rising from the heavy dew on the ground. The road, however, was seething with activity and the bustle of dozens of vehicles. Tractors pulling heavily laden tenders, lorries and horse-drawn transport, piled high with weird looking wooden structures which called to mind the heavy war and siege machines of a Roman army, passed in review. I could also make out the locally constructed light armoured cars of the Jewish Supernumerary Police, and the host of trekking men and women in their khaki and blue overalls. It was a cheerfully noisy scene to watch, and I was thinking of taking a sporting chance and following the procession to find out for myself what it was all about. At this moment Mike, a subaltern

of a dark-grey colour and was of a heavier type, to be used for the raising of grain and green fodder.

While we listened to the explanations of our guide, the two-hundred-odd men and girls who had arrived with the vehicles were breaking up into working gangs, which under the instructions of engineers and foremen made themselves busy about their tasks. Picks and shovels were unloaded and issued out to the labourers, who scattered along the pegged-out lines, to dig the foundations for the wooden structures of the tower, the walls and the huts. The J.S.P's, rifles at the ready, had taken up their position in a wide circle around the busy crowd, while others were guarding the tractors, which ploughed the soil as a token of final owner-ship. Numerous Arab children, reinforced in due course by their elders, were gathered round looking on with wonder at the frenzied activities of the Jews. When a heavy tractor had dragged the cumbersome parts of the wooden tower up the slope, and all hands assembled for the task of lifting it to settle in the founda-tion holes, even the townspeople and representatives of the Jewish colonization authorities divested themselves of their outer gar-ments to help with pulley and plank. After much shouting and a few unsuccessful launching attempts, the weird structure sank at last into its appointed place, accompanied by cries of satisfaction from the perspiring crowd. With that, the first part of the schedule appeared to have been completed, for the gong called the people to a frugal breakfast spread out on hastily improvised tables and benches.

I thought it then high time to take our leave, for my curiosity had been fully satisfied. Mike promised the girl and many other fellows who had joined our circle that he would come back in the evening, to see for himself how far the day's work had progressed. I did not omit to inquire of him the next morning how the place looked like in the evening.

'F-f-f-unny b-b-b-eggars', he began with an unusually pro-longed stutter, a sure indication of his mood. 'You would not recognise the place. The first thing that happened when I approached what looked like a fortified camp in mediæval times, was that a searchlight caught me in its cone, blinding me com-pletely. I was forced to put on the brakes. As I halted my car a fellow jumped on to the running board and asked me where I was driving to. When I mentioned the invitation to visit the place at night, he blew a whistle. The searchlight was turned off, and soon I could make out the wooden walls and their tarred boards and supporting beams. The track swung to the left and then sharply to the right and brought me straight to the gap in the wall. There were no gates, but the entrance was blocked by a thick barbed-wire knife-rest, which was pushed aside. I drove in and halted in front of the tower.'

I cannot recollect all the details which Mike related to me that morning and thereafter. The features which stand out in my memory now are that the dining hall and cookhouse were already complete with electric light; that water was running in the cook-house tap; that people slept in their huts, as yet without roofs and windows, and that old Mike had climbed the tower, and, helped by the searchlight, had seen the wall complete with fire slits and sandbagged watchpost. Oddly enough I can also recollect – strange how little details stick in one's mind – that Mike while looking down from the tower got the creeps when he suddenly found himself looking into glimmering eyes staring at him from the darkness. On investigating he was told that those were the eyes of the mules in the still half-open stables. Mike at any rate – not that he had much experience in such matters – failed to grasp how so much work could have been accomplished in a matter of ten hours by so few people. About fifty only had stayed behind, while the big crowd which had come with the procession had left again in the late hours of the afternoon.

That is as far as my contacts with the Jewish colonization in Palestine went. My dim recollections of those sights were revived on the occasion of a visit to an exhibition arranged for our benefit by Canadian P.O.W's. Graphs, diagrams, sketches and statistics, attractively drawn by artists, were there to demonstrate the riches of Canada, and the vast potential prosperity she was holding in trust for future development. Reuben, who was beside me, followed with shining eyes and envious exclamations the display of the treasures to be gained there by the hardy pioneer.

'We have a standard joke in Palestine', he said to me when we came out from the exhibition. 'It refers to the blunder old Moses made when he led the Hebrew tribes into Palestine. In the forty years wanderings which Moses had believed to be adequate for the retempering of the new generation, he could easily have reached a better place. And that without compromising his genius with hair-raising miracles. In extenuation one could find, how-ever, some good reasons for the choice of the old Hebrew. In

1300 B.C. Palestine must have shone like a glittering jewel in the eyes of his desert marauders. Canaan – as it was then called – was a highly-civilized and well-cultivated land. Such an unusual land with its irrigated orchards and walled-in towns must have appeared to my emaciated ancestors the paradise incarnate, and certainly wonderful enough to be claimed as the "Promised Land". Well, that was once upon a time, it looked quite different to my generation. We ascended to an eroded, desolate, and fever-stricken Canaan, having come from the rich pastures of Eastern and Central Europe. This time the attraction was not that of a sparkling gem. It was rather like the return of a prodigal son, who had no one to blame but himself for the abandonment of his patrimony. Three thousand years after Moses, the colonization of Palestine was an entirely different undertaking from the coloniza-tion of Canada or of South Africa.'

'What is the difference strictly speaking?' I asked, not quite satisfied with Reuben's hints.

'It should be quite evident', replied Reuben, with a sigh. 'In the case of Canada or South Africa, colonization is merely a question of adapting the plentiful resources of the country to the use of man. The hardy pioneer who walked out with an axe, a gun, some beads and blankets, found everything he could wish for on the spot. Timber, wild life, water stocked with fish, fertile land, rains in their seasons and an immediate return for his labour. Doubtless he knew hardships, and had to face dangers to life and property, but if he persevered he remained the conquering master of abundance and plenty. In Palestine, on the other hand, we are faced with almost exactly the opposite conditions. From the start we are confronted with the necessity of subsidising the country and, more important, the land. Only a life-time of giving to the land will eventually refund the money and faith invested in it. The possession of a gun – which, if not strictly legalised by a none-too-benevolent administration may land me in goal – does not fill a cooking pot there, and an axe has nothing to split unless it is timber imported from overseas. Water is there, but it must be coaxed up from the depths, and the soil must be recalled to its task by intricate processes of resurrection. Beads and blankets do not "buy" land – you pay for it in solid cash at speculative prices, provided you have managed to slip through the meshes of Government White Papers. Timber, iron, each head of cattle, seed, and much of our food supply had to be brought in ships, and many years went by before we came to enjoy the first fruits of our labour.

'Things have progressed a great deal since my community first took possession of its land. To-day new settlers can acquire most of their necessities and materials from supplies grown and made in the country. It is almost unbelievable that such changes have come about in a matter of fifteen or twenty years. The fact is that a small proportion of the country, which has been revived, is now providing a steadily increasing share of the equipment required for new colonization. Were it not for the acute shortage of capital, the development could have gone on at a much faster pace. Our colonization demands long-term investments, at a low rate of interest before it is in a position to pay. Every settlement in Palestine – be it an individual or a collective one – demands the exertions of almost a life-time before it can yield full sustenance to its toilers as well as a refund of the colonization credits. During the first twenty years, the standard of living of the settler will slowly rise from zero, at which he begins – until it reaches the level of a well-paid skilled worker – where it finally stops. Personally I doubt whether mixed farming in Palestine or anywhere else, for that matter, will ever secure a higher standard. That is the reason why capitalistic enterprise has never entered the field of mixed farming in Palestine, and I am not the man to regret it. By keeping mixed farming, which must remain the foundation of regenerated Judaea, solidly on nationally-owned soil and in the hands of collective or co-operative settlements, we secure the future of a self-supporting Jewish peasantry. The collective and co-operative organisation of such a peasantry makes it possible to maintain in the villages a high standard of social and cultural life, which in turn becomes the means of binding the younger generations securely to the soil.'

Reuben exercised minute care in giving me a precise picture of the growth of an agricultural entity which, to him, is the cornerstone of the new Jewish society in Palestine. He traced for my pleasure every phase of the development, beginning with the trek and finishing ten or fifteen years later when the life of the community had taken on the aspect of a stable and healthy organism.

And again – as so often before in this story – Reuben's associations and clashes with Nature were of a singular character. It seemed to me that for Reuben, and his town- and Ghetto-bred companions, Nature was always an almost holy entity. She never became for them the commonplace actuality which she is with us. In Reuben's youth Nature was to him the 'Being' of the polytheist; then again, on his training farm she became a grim yet seducing siren to be conquered and subdued, and now once more, mayhap for the last time, Nature exacted from him yet another tribute. Reuben saw her now as the one who takes her toll of life, an outrageous, senseless extinguisher of the very marvel of life to which she gave birth.

'It is not so simple, Jack, what we call striking root in the soil' – Reuben admonished me on one occasion. 'In fact, it is never *done* – it is rather a process of Becoming. You cannot set the pace for it, because you can neither harry nor harass Nature. She follows her own clock and to make her time-table your own – you must be born with it and have had it in your blood for generations. Look at it from the materialistic point of view of the farmer who has to live by her graces. He may play on her all the tricks of modern science: may feed her soil with the latest fertiliser, or with the primeval dung; he may fight one set of destructive parasites by breeding another set of benevolent ones; select and mate his seeds and breeding stock; plough deep into the bowels of the earth to make fecund new, unexploited strata of the subsoil; level and plane the surface; drain and irrigate the water resources; he may do these and the other hundred and one things which accumulated experience and pioneering research work have taught him, but can he alter the seasons and know the unknowable? He may endeavour to dictate and force the issue, but can he foresee the consequences? We, for instance, came to our land thirsty and hungry, hasty, and high-handed, equipped with much cunning and alertness, and she defeated us nevertheless time and again.

'The answer to that riddle is written on the face and in the soul of the peasant. The creases of impatience *She* smoothes out and replaces them by the wrinkles of gentleness; rashness and temper are conquered, and only the steadfastness of humility remains. You see now our desires and longings were simple: to walk the earth as her honest sons and not as cunning rebels; to live at peace with the powers which have the last word in matters of life or death – to acquire such a rhythm of life – became for us the imperative prerequisite of survival. For those begotten by men of the soil, bred and grown up in direct contact with the earth, such harmony with nature comes subconsciously. The rhythm of growth and decay; of infinite bliss and abysmal suffering, the intrinsic harmony of the seasons, are communicated in the blood-stream to the rustic babe.

'For people of my kidney, even when born and bred in the country, the earth and the seasons meant no more than a swim in summer and tobogganing in the winter. We knew little besides and went back to nature with the confidence of the theorist. Was not everything worked out in advance? Is the clay to command Reason? The resulting clash was inevitable. We met in fiery conflict with the malign Powers, who dared to spoil our plans and frustrate our will. It was a bitter heart-rending struggle, in which we were knocked down dazed and wounded; but we managed somehow to rise on our battered limbs and fight on again. Such deadly contests have knocked some sense into us – to be sure – but candidly speaking, the metamorphosis of *town-bred* and *brain-fed* people into peasants is unlikely to materialise within one generation. It warms one's heart to look at the deeply-furrowed and benevolent faces of our first pioneers. You see there the reflection of the newly-established harmony between men and Nature. But, uncover their breasts and look into their hearts and you will still find the remnants of scorn and wilfulness there, age-long environment still plays with them her destructive rôle. There are people among us who deplore the coarsening of the intellectual fibres which must result from our return to a peasant way of life; they suggest that the next generation, born and bred on the land of a proletarian community, will never attain the intellectual standards of their parents. To my mind there is much in what such critics suggest, but I am not the man to regret it. We shall, as a matter of course, lose much of our over-rated and envied intellectuality, but we shall gain in greatly-needed health and culture in its truer sense. That our sons and daughters will not be flitting from capital to capital, assimilating the many abhorrent trends of modernism, is a great source of satisfaction to me. I hope they will be the happier for the loss of such contacts; they will certainly be the better for gaining other contacts of no less subtlety and of a more invigorating character. We are not afraid of exchanging refinement for sturdiness, and speculative commercialism for scientific and upright service to the soil.

'I fear that at the risk of verbosity, even pomposity, I have tried to give you a clear idea of our desires.'

I continue to give here the whole length of Reuben's monologue –for as he talked I got the impression that I was forgotten by him. I dared not interrupt him because I had a feeling that I was eavesdropping on a confessional. And I knew that Reuben was approaching fast the last station of our communion. Victory was already in sight beyond the barbed wire . . .

After clearing his throat he almost whispered on:

'It is only the romanticism of the town people which sees in the powers of nature nothing but sweet benign bliss. As for the sailor, so for the tiller of the soil, nature offers a good measure of malice and of chaotic evil. When the new settler in the wild, untamed wilderness crashes face to face with such phenomena, no poetical rhapsodies are likely to well up in his heart; instead there will be tears, impotent rage and curses. Take Ruth, for instance, and her fellow-workers of both sexes, who lavished so much loving care on our tree nursery.

'Ruth had worked this branch for many years before we settled on our own land. She brought to the newly-planted tree nursery in our settlement much experience, training, and furthermore, a most tender and yet efficient mother touch. There was nothing she left undone to protect her baby seedlings and saplings from the furies of the elements. Everything seemed to prosper and grow under her management. In the course of two years, the tree nursery became the most attractive part of the building settlement. Then one dreadful day came disaster. A desert wind, Hamsin, laden with dust and of a fiery energy, turned Ruth's kingdom into desolation. Not a sprig of green was left standing, all the plants were burned into rusty cinders, and within a couple of hours the work and sweat of two years was turned to dust. Poor Ruth collapsed into an hysterical coma, which lasted for two days – but it took her and her companions more time than that to bring themselves to go back to the field of slaughter to clear the shambles for a new beginning. You will probably remark with the same "honesty" and "kindness" which many of us males use when talking about women – no wonder! it is only natural for a weak woman to break out into hysterics. A woman! Ruth has never, before or since, succumbed to hysterics, not even on that memorable night during the riots when everything appeared chaotic; our wheatfields were on fire, bullets were whistling round our ears, and Ruth alone proceeded with the coolest nerve to handle the sleepy and frightened babies and their stampeding mothers: it was our first experience of that nature.

'Ruth, with her long pale face framed by coal-black pigtails and her sinuous slim body was not a personality to submit to defeat by having hysterics. Nevertheless, she broke down on that day when the desert wind choked the life out of her fragrant kingdom of citrus and cypress, pine and larch, myrtle and rose-bush – all of which had been destined to live and to give shelter and life to men and crops. What struck so deeply at Ruth was not the irretrievable loss of toil and time; but rather the utter malice and unfathomable savageness of nature. For her, Nature was until then her own sister, helping her with her tender lusty seedlings, the marvel of the giant gum tree growing from a tiny fragment of matter. When Ruth returned to her work she had forsaken her one-sided view of Nature, and she approached her with mental reservations; never again would it be all love and tenderness; there would always be grave suspicion and grim scepticism. Ruth came to understand what the tillers of the soil had learned throughout the ages, by experience and heredity: the grim struggle for food and survival, which had made man both cunning and superstitious, humble and proud.

'It was such a day a year later on which Sheba's poultry yard was decimated. She had under her care six henhouses, built of concrete and roofed with corrugated iron sheets, which housed a few thousand Leghorn hens. A fifteen hundred egg incubator hatching had been released a few weeks prior to that calamitous day, and the chicks were already strutting about. Sheba and her fellow-workers had taken every conceivable precaution to shelter the winged swarm from heatwaves. The roofs and walls of the henhouses were regularly drenched to cool the air inside, and wet canvas shutters were ready at hand to moisten the penetrating blast when necessary. But of what avail were such feeble devices of men against the evil offspring of the desert? When Sheba's desperate cry: "My chicks are suffocating", reached my ears, I was crouching in a pit over which stood a tractor under repair. When my pal and I scrambled out and stepped into the hazy, hot merciless sun, we immediately felt the change which had taken place in the weather. There was no stormy wind. On the contrary, the air stood still, simmering in the oppressive, slightly veiled blaze of the mid-day sun during a Palestinian May. I knew enough of Sheba to understand that such an appeal coming from her meant serious trouble, for Sheba – a staunch and relentless suffragette – kept all male interference well outside her own domain. Although not in the least fanatical – how could she, a buxom, benign mother of three children, be fanatical – she was determined nevertheless to keep the agricultural branches which were the prerogative of the womenfolk – out of the spiritual and physical grasp of the males. We rushed down the slope in the wake of many others who were hurrying from workshops and sheds. But when we arrived at the poultry-yard our help was no longer required; Sheba had everything under control and a mass disaster was warded off in the nick of time. But unfortunately there were a few hundred casualties among the younger brood of chicks, which were already too far gone to recover from the sudden assault of the heat wave. Hardy Sheba wept bitterly when she committed the innocent victims to the flames.

'The following winter we had to contend with a flood, which drowned acres upon acres of winter potatoes and cabbages, and destroyed the lower sections of our three-year-old citrus plantation.

'Well, old man, you have now heard enough of what we suffer at stepmother Nature's hands. Ravages were repaired, improvements made, and a keener awareness of the potential destructive powers in Nature's elements added at last that touch of realism which, though new to us, is very familiar to farmers of experience. These are just a few details of our struggle to become one with the great family of farming people the world over just in case I have misled you to believe that life in Palestine is all milk and honey.'

Listening to Reuben, one might have been tempted to believe that he and his comrades spent most of their time in either cheating the elements or in being cheated by them. In fact, philosophical speculations seldom, if ever, occupied their minds and certainly not in the foundation years of their settlement. In those years they obeyed one command only, and that was work, obeyed with what appears to me an awe-inspiring intensity. For once development was tapped, an unbroken chain of urgencies sped them on their way. The beginnings were always on a small scale – they had to be, for lack of capital. But when irrigation pipes for five acres of vegetables and green fodder were laid out it was found that an additional number of cows could be maintained, and that more poultry could be supported simply on the scrapings of the vegetable garden. One branch in the farm became inevitably the sponsor of another, and that meant more work, more people and machinery.

Reuben's community followed willingly the pace set by the

growth of living matter. Branch was added to branch, and brick to brick, until the complete edifice of a collective economy, with its agricultural and industrial ramifications, triumphantly emerged. The members of the community employed on outside work were called in, and a settled society of men and women and their offspring, replaced the former semi-nomadic way of life of the seekers for work and pasture. A variety of economic, educational and political activities completed the material framework of the society. In the scheme of things devised by the Jewish pioneers in Palestine, the collective, as indeed every type of social organisation of and for the working classes, is just one of the many integral cells of the whole society. If each budding social cell were left to itself, its annihilation through the adoption of the Levantine outlook on life, might have come on it swiftly and inevitably.

The Labour movement in Palestine has had the wisdom – I quote Reuben – to make full and expedient use of the objective conditions of the country. For there is much scope and opportunity in a desolate countryside and in the emptiness of space. Unhampered by vested interests, social or ideological, new forms of life and of civilization may be cast. And on that tiny strip of the globe the daring attempt was actually made, to subject up-to-date scientific knowledge to the guiding force of a higher social morality.

Labour in Palestine was indeed founded and developed as an organic Society comprising every activity and form of self-expression of the working men and women. The peculiar conditions, under which the Jewish reconstruction work in Palestine has had to be done, favoured Labour with the opportunity of turning its main effort to the making of a new society, in which party politics became the handmaid but not the master.

The Jewish intellect, stubbornly lured by the search for the infinite, was now again forced into the fertile groove of social creation.

Reuben and his friends are confident that their goal is in sight.